A2 Geography
UNIT 4

AQA

Specification

A

Module 4: Challenge and Change
in the Natural Environment

Philip Allan Updates
Market Place
Deddington
Oxfordshire
OX15 0SE

tel: 01869 338652
fax: 01869 337590
e-mail: sales@philipallan.co.uk
www.philipallan.co.uk

© Philip Allan Updates 2002
ISBN 0 86003 685 5

This Guide has been written specifically to support students preparing for the
AQA Specification A A2 Geography Unit 4 examination. The content has been
neither approved nor endorsed by AQA and remains the sole responsibility of
the author.

Printed by Raithby, Lawrence & Co. Ltd, Leicester

Contents

Introduction

■ ■ ■

Content Guidance

■ ■ ■

Questions and Answers

Introduction

About this guide

This guide is for A2 Geography students following the AQA Specification A course. It aims to guide you through Unit 4, which examines the content of **Module 4: Challenge and Change in the Natural Environment**.

This guide will clarify:

- the content of the module so that you know and understand what you have to learn
- the nature of the unit test
- the geographical skills and techniques you will need to know
- the standards you will need to reach to achieve a particular grade
- the examination techniques you will require to improve your performance and maximise your achievement

This Introduction describes the structure of A2 Geography and outlines the aims of Module 4. It then provides an explanation of some of the key command words used in examination papers. There is also advice concerning geographical skills, and learning and revision techniques.

The Content Guidance section summarises the essential information of Module 4. It is designed to make you aware of the material that has to be covered and learnt, and of the underlying synoptic links with other elements within this and other modules. The appreciation of these links is essential at A-level.

The Question and Answer section provides sample questions and candidate responses at C-grade and A-grade level. Each answer is followed by a detailed examiner's response. It is suggested that you read through the relevant topic area in the Content Guidance section before attempting a question from the Question and Answer section and only read the specimen answers after you have tackled the question yourself.

The essay in this unit is synoptic. It assesses the candidate's knowledge and understanding across a range of subject matter and expects you to make links between the different aspects of geography covered in this and other modules.

A2 Geography

Many of you will have taken the AS examination at the end of the first year of a 2 year course. You have decided to continue to study for another year to take A-level, which will be maintained at the traditional A-level standard. However, some of you may be taking AS at the same time as A2, at the end of a 1 or 2 year programme.

AS Geography covers three of the six modules that contribute to the full A-level qualification. These are set out below to remind you of what you have covered in the AS. In order to demonstrate synopticity in the essay, you can refer to work you have covered in AS as well as A2.

Remember that A-level cannot be taken without AS; it is not a qualification in its own right.

AS

Unit 1		Unit 2		Unit 3		
Core Concepts in Physical Geography	+	Core Concepts in Human Geography	+	Geographical Skills	=	**AS Geography**
35% of AS marks ($17\frac{1}{2}$% of A-level marks)		35% of AS marks ($17\frac{1}{2}$% of A-level marks)		30% of AS marks (15% of A-level marks)		

A-level (AS plus the following)

Unit 4		Unit 5		Fieldwork Investigation — Unit 6		
Challenge and Change in the Natural Environment	+	Challenge and Change in the Human Environment	+	Coursework **or Unit 7** Written Alternative	=	**A-level Geography**
15% of marks		15% of marks		20% of marks		

The aims of Module 4

This module aims to help you:
- learn and apply knowledge and understanding of physical processes and their interactions and outcomes over space and time
- understand the influence people have on these processes and the effects the processes have on people
- apply this knowledge and understanding at a variety of scales
- develop an understanding of the relationships between people and their environments, and of the opportunities, challenges and constraints that face people in different places and environments
- learn and apply geographical skills
- understand that geography is dynamic
- reflect the importance of people's and your own values and attitudes to issues and questions
- acquire a deeper understanding of the connections between different aspects of geography
- develop a greater ability to synthesise geographical information

These aims are very broad and can be applied to any study of physical geography. After the study of the module, you will be able to demonstrate your understanding of the specified areas of physical geography. You will also be able to use the relevant geographical skills, interpret what they reveal and be aware of the values and conflicts that arise from the study of geography.

Assessment objectives

There are four ways in which these are assessed in this unit:
- AO1 — Knowledge = (27%)
- AO2 — Critical understanding = (33%)
- AO3 — Application of knowledge and critical understanding to unfamiliar contexts (27%)
- AO4 — Selection and use of skills and techniques, including communication, appropriate to geographical studies (13%)

Remember that every mark gained is in response to you demonstrating these in your answers. Making sure that your answers are relevant to the question is therefore essential.

Examination skills

Before looking at typical examination questions and responses in the Question and Answer section, we will examine the broader skills that are essential for success in the examination. These fall into two areas: the meaning of the command words, and making the most effective use of the examination paper.

The importance of command words

Command words are used by the examiners to tell you what to do in order to answer examination questions effectively. The words are set out below, in an approximate order of difficulty, with an explanation of what they mean. All of these may be familiar from AS, with the addition of 'evaluate' and 'discuss' which are considered to be higher-level command words and thus more appropriate to A2.

Command word(s)	Meaning
Describe...	State simply what is requested. Explanation or further comment is not required.
Name/State...	Identify briefly. One word may be adequate, but it may be better to use a sentence if in any doubt.
Distinguish between...	Define and state the differences between. Linking terms, such as 'whereas' or 'on the other hand', are essential.
Outline...	Describe, with a specific focus, the geographical element requested. For example, 'Outline the main features of...' has more of a focus than 'Describe the main features of...'

Outline the reasons for...	Give reasons for, with a specific focus, the geographical element required. The response will be briefer than a full explanation.
Account for/ Explain/Why...?	Give reasons for. The marks will be awarded for these reasons, rather than for description.
Give reason(s) for...	Some explanation must be offered.
Describe and explain...	Both elements, description and explanation, must be present for full marks. Ensure that examples of the mentioned theme are used in the response.
Compare...	What are the similarities between? Some element of contrast may be present.
Contrast...	What are the differences between? Two separate accounts will not meet the needs of this command; there must be a specific contrast or distinction between the elements.
Examine...	Give an overview of the elements which affect the theme, i.e. outline and explain.
Assess/To what extent...?	This requires an assessment of the importance of the factors involved in the response. This would be in an extended prose answer, rather than a short one.
Evaluate...	This is an alternative to 'To what extent', and has an emphasis on the *relative* importance of the factors/ themes involved. It is likely to need an essay response. A conclusion should be reached.
Discuss...	This requires a full coverage of the themes, again needing an essay response, with a reasoned conclusion. A variety of themes, strategies and results should be covered.

The unit test

Module 4 is assessed by Unit 4. You have 1 hour 30 minutes to answer this paper, which accounts for 15% of the A-level Geography qualification. The paper is divided into two sections: resource-based questions in Section A and essay questions in Section B.

Section A

In Section A, there are three stimulus–response questions, one from each of the three elements: (1) Coast processes and problems, (2) Geomorphological processes and hazards and (3) Cold environments and human activity. You have to answer *two* questions from Section A.

Each question is marked out of 15, so there are 30 marks for the stimulus–response questions, out of 90 for the whole paper. You are advised to spend about 30 minutes on Section A. This advice is on the front of the examination paper, and means you have about 15 minutes per question, including a little time for the selection of the questions.

The spacing on the stimulus–response questions allows two lines per mark for your response, which is written in the question book. It is therefore useful to allocate your time accordingly. The highest number of marks is for the last part, so you should allow just under half the time on each question for this section — about 7 minutes.

Try to keep within the lines allocated, but if this proves to be impossible, use the lined pages at the end of the question booklet, making sure that you have clearly indicated what you have done and have identified each response.

Response levels

Parts (a) and (b) of each stimulus–response question are given 4 marks, generally by point marking, but part (c) (7 marks) is marked according to Levels. There are criteria for reaching these Levels depending on the quality of the geographical content and the use of geographical and English language. This part of each question will require a fuller development of geographical understanding and language skills.

The Levels are as follows:

- **Level 1** responses are basic, with perhaps one or two points without examples, and a simplistic style of writing that is not focused on the requirements of the question. Specialist vocabulary is lacking.
- **Level 2** responses show a clear understanding of the topic, with better use of language, and have points with examples that recognise the potential complexity of the subject matter. There is appropriate use of specialist vocabulary.
- **Level 3** responses show detailed understanding, include several points with examples, and are written in a sophisticated and effective style. There is confident use of specialist vocabulary and a focus on the requirements of the question.

The command words are important, so make sure you remember to follow the instructions.

Section B

There are three essay questions in Section B, one from each of the three elements of the module. You have to answer one question from these three. They are marked out of 30 and the mark is doubled to give a mark out of 60, out of a total of the 90 marks available on the whole paper. The advice is to spend 60 minutes on this section, including planning time.

The questions are one-part essays, and advice to candidates about the need for synopticity appears above the essay titles. The essays are wide ranging in subject in order to allow candidates to develop synoptic themes using other elements of the specification. Fuller details can be found in the Question and Answer section of this guide.

Your answers are written in the question book. Several lined pages are supplied for this purpose. (If you do not have enough sheets, additional sheets can be requested; please make sure that you attach these firmly to the question book.)

Response levels

Essays are marked by means of Levels, of which there are five in all, as follows:

- **Level 1** A very weak answer with little attempt to follow the theme. A low level of knowledge and understanding is shown, and the answer is very inaccurate and poorly organised. Poor communication skills are shown, with many errors in spelling and grammar.
- **Level 2** A very mediocre answer, only occasionally relevant to the theme. Decidedly deficient in knowledge and understanding, with interrelationships lacking relevance and an increasingly descriptive response which may drift into another answer. Support is scanty and frequently inaccurate. Communication skills are basic, including many errors in spelling and grammar.
- **Level 3** A satisfactory answer at the upper end and mediocre at the lower end of the band. There is a reasonable grasp of knowledge, but understanding is suspect in places. The interconnections between elements of the specification are briefly mentioned. Support is not detailed, is occasionally inaccurate and is inconsistent. Communication skills are appropriate.
- **Level 4** A good answer, remaining relevant to the theme. Evaluation is implicit, with a confident range of knowledge, but with some omissions. There is reference to a range of subject matter from other elements of the specification (synoptic). Support is present but not always detailed. Communication skills are effective.
- **Level 5** A very good answer, consistently relevant to the theme. There is explicit evaluation and the command words are clearly followed, with the use of appropriate terminology and a confident range of knowledge from across the elements of the specification (synoptic). Support is consistent, accurate and detailed and communication skills are detailed and sophisticated.

It is not possible to reach the top two mark bands without the synoptic links, which show the interrelationships between different elements of the specification, being identified clearly.

The examiners are looking for good organisation in these answers, so an introduction, a full development of the points to be made and a conclusion are very important. It is essential to have a plan; many candidates note points on the page before starting the essay. The suggested time for the essay question allows time for planning.

The introduction should set the scene. It does not have to be lengthy, but might include a definition of the terms used or the statement of the ideas to be developed.

The points to be developed usually appear as a series of paragraphs, one for each point, related to the theme of the question. The use of named and located cases is essential to ensure a good mark, as is the development of the interrelationships between the elements of the specification.

The conclusion in an essay summarises the main points made and refers to the question set. Remember to check the command words.

Geographical skills

As an integral part of your studies for this unit, you are required to develop and under-stand a variety of skills. The six types of geographical skill specified at AS are still relevant. These are:

- basic skills
- graphical skills
- cartographic skills
- ICT (information and communication technology) skills
- statistical skills
- investigative skills

A number of additional skills are specified for A2. The skills specified for AS are simply listed here. The A2 skills are described in more detail.

Basic skills

The levels of accuracy, sophistication and detail for the following basic skills are expected to be greater at A2:

- Base maps
- Sketch maps
- Atlas
- Photographs

Literacy

You need further to develop literacy skills during the A2 course. The assessment units require the ability to respond to both resource-based (structured) questions and essays.

Graphical skills

You should be familiar with the majority of these skills, but some will be new to you. You are expected to be able to interpret and construct the following:

- Line graphs — four types are specified
  - simple line graphs
  - comparative line graphs
  - compound line graphs
  - divergent line graphs
- Bar graphs — four types are specified
  - simple bar graphs
  - comparative bar graphs
  - compound (or divided) bar graphs
  - divergent bar graphs
- Scattergraphs — and the use of the best fit line
- Pie charts
- Triangular graphs

- Lorenz curves
- Storm hydrographs
- Kite and vector diagrams
- Pyramids
- Dispersion diagrams — these show the spread of data. They are usually in graph (point distribution) format, for example showing annual glacier melting rates. They show the mean and interquartile range.

Cartographic skills

- Ordnance Survey maps
- Soil maps
- Choropleth (shading) and isoline maps
- Base maps — many of the graphical techniques listed above can be plotted on base maps.
- Maps with proportional symbols — squares, circles, semicircles or bars can be used to show values in a two-dimensional format. A greater range of values can be shown than on a linear representation, because the symbols increase in area rather than linearly. For instance, a value 100 times greater can be shown using a square with sides only 10 times greater (e.g. on a map showing amounts spent on hazard management in different countries).
- Maps showing movement — flow lines can be used on maps to show volumes of movement. The lines are proportional in width to the amount moved, for example on a map showing the transport of minerals from cold environments to MEDCs. Trip and desire lines show the start and finish points of individual movements, for example the movements of tourists on sand dune systems.

ICT (information and communication technology) skills

- Photographs
- Satellite images
- Databases
- Internet
- Video and television programmes
- Geographic information systems (GIS) — these are more flexible than standard databases, and link greater amounts of geographical data, including census data, local authority information, OS maps and satellite data.

Statistical skills

- Measures of central tendency — mean, mode and median
- Means of dispersion — interquartile range and standard deviation
- Correlation tests — at A2, in addition to **Spearman's rank correlation coefficient**, you need to be familiar with **Pearson's product moment correlation coefficient**. This is a more complicated, but more accurate, method of testing whether a relationship exists between sets of data. It measures the degree to

which a change in one variable is associated with changes in the other. It is used on data shown on a scattergraph and the outcome is a positive or negative relationship. The results are always within the range +1.0 (perfect positive correlation) to –1.0 (perfect negative correlation). It follows that a result closer to 0 indicates a weaker relationship (more like a clustered distribution). The minimum number of pairs of data is 6, although a minimum of 10 pairs ensures greater reliability. The test is very frequently used, for example on the relationship between glacial retreat and average global temperatures. At A2, you are expected to understand significance which, for Pearson, is calculated using the student's *t*-test (see below).

- Comparative tests. The **chi-squared** test is used to compare the frequency distribution of two sets of variables. It does not measure correlation, but the association between the two sets of data. Observed frequencies (O) are compared with expected frequencies (E), and the probability of the differences occurring by chance is assessed. Data should always be in raw number form, with at least 20 values. A contingency table is constructed to compare E and O. The resulting individual cell values in this should show an expected frequency of 5 or more. If not, the categories (columns or rows) should be merged. The **Mann-Whitney test** is used when ranked data and data in the form of frequencies need to be compared, or where ranked samples of unequal size exist. The **student's *t*-test** is used to measure the significance of a test and a given level of confidence for a particular sample size.

- Spatial distribution. **Nearest neighbour analysis** is used to measure the spatial distribution of data, in terms of the degree of clustering. At least 30 samples should be plotted on a map. The calculated result, which ranges from 0 to 2.14, can be shown by a linear scale, where 2.14 indicates perfect regularity, 1.0 indicates a random distribution, 0.23 linear clustering and 0 perfect clustering.

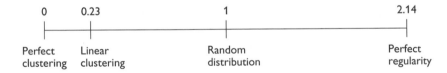

- The **index of dispersion** is frequently used with the **centre of gravity**. It measures the average distance of a feature from the 'centre of gravity' (the average of the coordinates of the feature). The degree of clustering is then demonstrated by the index of dispersion, drawn as a circle on a map, indicating a more clustered feature where the circle has a smaller radius.

- **Significance levels** indicate the probability of a result occurring by chance, and are usually assessed at a probability of 10%, 5% or 1%, the lower values being the more reliable. Statistical tables are available for this purpose. To use significance, a hypothesis (H_1) and a null hypothesis (H_0) have to be established. If the result is significant, H_0 is rejected and H_1 is accepted.

Investigative skills

- The identification of geographical questions and issues.
- The selection of relevant primary and secondary data and an assessment of their validity.
- The processing, presentation, analysis and interpretation of the evidence collected.
- The ability to draw conclusions and show an awareness of their validity.
- The awareness of risks when undertaking fieldwork. Investigative skills are best developed by a programme of fieldwork undertaken in the AS and A2 years. Preparation for work in the field, the collection of data and their interpretation and evaluation are demonstrated clearly by writing up the fieldwork in the format suggested by the board. Your teachers will be able to advise you about this. At A2, the assessment of these skills takes place in Units 6 or 7.

At A2, greater emphasis is placed on the development of the stages of the enquiry, the drawing of conclusions and their validity.

Techniques for learning and revision

As in AS, there is no surplus of time available for teaching the subject content at A2. You must ensure that, from the very start of your course, you establish good working practices to make the most of the time available:

- It is important not to fall behind with work during the year. New material will be taught each week, so, if you are unavoidably absent (e.g. because of illness), do make sure you are able to make up the missed work as quickly as possible.
- You will probably have a steady stream of homework during the course. This is likely to take a variety of forms, ranging from working from the textbook or other sources, to practising examination questions.
- Read widely from a variety of sources, including your textbook, newspapers and magazines such as *Geography Review*. Television programmes are also relevant. The information you gather will enable you to develop a number of case studies for use in your examination answers.

The specification is divided up into modules, as we have already seen. Each module is divided into three elements and each of these into five sub-elements.

Module 4: Challenge and Change in the Natural Environment is divided as follows:

Elements	Sub-elements
Coast processes and problems	The coast and marine energy Marine erosional processes and landforms Marine depositional processes and landforms Coastal problems Coastal management strategies

Geomorphological processes and hazards	Plate tectonics and landforms Volcanic activity Earthquakes Weathering and mass movement The impact of, and response to, geomorphological processes and hazards
Cold environments and human activity	The environment Glacial and periglacial processes and landforms Biomes and ecosystems Human activity, economic processes and resource management Present problems and future issues

Revision can be more easily structured by taking the sub-elements and focusing on them. Note that it is better to revise the sub-elements in the order in which they appear, or there is the risk that points will not make sense!

Some tips on revision

- Having selected a topic for revision, read and learn the material you have for this topic, for example notes, handouts, worksheets etc.
- Refer to your textbooks and to this publication. You might also find Raw, M. (2000) *AS/A-Level Geography Exam Revision Notes* (Philip Allan Updates) a useful guide.
- Learn the relevant case studies. You will need one or two for each element/sub-element and these should be at the specified scales.
- Practise sample questions, keeping to the appropriate timings. Use the questions in the last section of this guide for this purpose, taking care not to look at the sample answers and examiner's comments until you have attempted the questions. There are other specimen questions available, so consult your teacher/lecturer for advice.
- Apply your knowledge and understanding when practising so that your answers reflect the demands of the question.
- Allow yourself adequate time for revision. Little and often is usually better than concentrated pressure at the last minute.

Content
Guidance

There are three elements in the specification content for Module 4:

(1) Coast processes and problems

(2) Geomorphological processes and hazards

(3) Cold environments and human activity

In this section, the key concepts of each of these topics are explained, together with a breakdown of what you need to know and learn.

Points to note

- You are able to select two of the three elements for study, but this will reduce question choice. On the other hand, it will make the content much more manageable.
- Your teacher/lecturer will usually make the selection. You may need to be aware of the synoptic links with the element not studied.
- The number of references to case studies may seem daunting, but one or two case studies for each element is usually sufficient.
- All synoptic links in the specification are included in this section.

Coast processes and problems

The coast and marine energy

Definitions

The coast is the interface between land and sea. It is influenced by marine, terrestrial, atmospheric and human factors, and is considered to be one of the most dynamic environments.

You need to:
- be able to define the coast and be aware of the factors that influence its formation

The coast as a system

The coast is a system which has inputs and outputs of energy. It is constantly changing as the inputs of energy vary both spatially and temporally (over time). Negative feedback is more common in the long term, but there will be periodic bursts of energy causing positive feedback in the short term, for example under severe storm conditions.

Inputs	Outputs
• Wave energy	• Loss of wave energy
• Tides	• Depositional landforms:
• Currents	– beaches
• Winds	– mudflats
• Storm surges	– sand dunes
• Tidal waves (tsunami)	– coral reefs
• Changes in sea level	• Erosional landforms:
• Sediment	– cliffs
• Human activities	– shore platforms

Spatial variations in energy are a result of variations in the strength of the wind, the fetch, and the number and intensity of storms. Storms are most frequent in mid-latitudes where low-pressure systems (depressions) are frequent and in the tropics where tropical low-pressure systems (hurricanes) occur. The shape of the coastline, in terms of shelter or exposure, is also important.

Temporal variations are those involving seasonal or even daily differences. In the mid-latitudes, for example, depressions are more frequent in winter, whereas hurricanes occur in late summer. In addition, there are significant variations in energy between storms and the calmer periods between them.

Open coastlines in high latitudes are high-energy and are dominated by erosion. This is a result of high wave and wind activity. Low-energy coasts are sheltered and are dominated by deposition. This is a result of low wave and wind, but greater tide, activity.

You need to:
- know about inputs to and outputs from the coastal system
- be aware that these inputs and outputs can vary both spatially and temporally
- distinguish between high- and low-energy coasts

Energy inputs — waves

Waves are the main input of energy into the coastal system. They are caused by the action of wind as it blows over the surface of the water. The energy in a wave moves orbitally, moving forward only near the shore where friction slows the base of the wave. The energy in a wave is affected by the fetch — the maximum distance of open sea the wave can travel. Waves with the longest fetch have the greatest impact on the coast. The depth of water affects wave energy too, as shallow water offshore reduces the energy reaching the coast. Wind strength and duration also affect the size of the waves.

There are two types of wave: surfing or spilling (destructive) and surging (constructive). Spilling waves are high-energy, with steep profiles. They tend to pull material down the beach in a strong backwash and weak swash, thus steepening the profile towards the upper end and reducing it towards the lower. They occur frequently, about 10–14 per minute, and have a short wavelength (about 20 metres).

Surging (constructive) waves are low-energy, with shallower profiles. They tend to carry material up the beach in a strong swash and weak backwash, thus increasing material at the top of the beach. They occur less frequently, at about 6–8 per minute, and have a long wavelength (up to 100 metres), the result of swell and a long fetch.

You need to:
- be aware of the causes of waves and the factors affecting wave energy
- understand the nature of spilling (destructive) and surging (constructive) waves and their impact on the coastal energy system

Energy inputs — tides and currents

Tides are the result of the gravitational pull of the Moon and the Sun, and centrifugal force. The diurnal tidal interval (12 hours 26 minutes) is caused by the Moon's gravitational pull closest to the Earth, with a second wave on the opposite side of the globe caused by centrifugal force. When the Sun, Moon and Earth are aligned every 2 weeks, spring tides occur, and when they are at 90° to each other, neap tides occur.

Tides produce powerful currents that transport large amounts of water and sediment. Large tidal ranges are dominated by landforms such as mudflats, salt marshes and estuaries; small ranges allow wave action to be more important, producing beaches, bars and barrier islands.

Large-scale currents are the result of prevailing winds, such as the North Atlantic Drift, driven by the westerlies.

You need to:
- understand the causes of tides
- know that tidal range affects the type of landforms
- be aware that currents are the result of prevailing winds

Energy inputs — storm surges and tidal waves

Storm surges are the accumulation of water on the coast, and have a far greater effect than tides. Two areas frequently affected by such phenomena are the Bay of Bengal (tropical cyclones) and the North Sea (mid-latitude depressions). In both cases, the sea level rises, as these are areas of low pressure. The effect is increased by waves being driven ahead of the storm by the strong winds that accompany such events. The shape of the coastline, channelling the water into a funnel shape, is also important. The surges can be intensified when they occur in conjunction with spring tides and high river discharge.

Tidal waves, or tsunami, are the result of under-sea earthquakes. These events send out submarine shock waves that become more prominent in the shallow water close to land. They are more destructive near to the epicentre and decrease in intensity further away.

You need to:
- know the causes and effects of storm surges
- know regional case studies, such as the North Sea and the Bay of Bengal
- understand the causes and effects of tidal waves

Coastal sediment cells

Coastal sediment comes from a variety of sources, including the seabed, beaches, river channels/estuaries and erosion from cliffs.

The coast can be divided into sediment cells. Sediment is eroded, moved and deposited within, but very rarely between, these cells. Thus, the removal of sediment from a cell results in permanent loss, as it cannot be replaced. Variations in energy inputs also impact within these cells. There are 11 sediment cells along the coastline of England and Wales. The sediment cell is the basic unit of coastal management in the UK.

You need to:
- know the sources of sediment
- understand the concept of the sediment cell
- be aware of the importance of sediment cells in coastal processes
- study a small-scale coastline, using OS maps to analyse change over time

Energy loss — wave refraction

Wave energy is dissipated at (or close to) the coast, mainly as a result of friction. This can be explained by refraction. As waves approach the coast, they start to refract, i.e. align themselves increasingly parallel to the coast. This is the result of friction causing the base of the waves in the shallow water near the headland, which is reached first, to be retarded. This causes the waves to become higher and steeper, reduced in velocity and wavelength and to focus on the headland, producing a concentration of energy which results in erosion at the headland.

In contrast, away from the headland, the waves lose energy by friction in the shallower water. As a result, they are lower and less steep, have an increase in velocity and wavelength and produce low energy in the bays. The reduction in wave energy in the bays encourages deposition and, in addition, currents are set up which carry eroded sediment from the headland to the bays (as in sediment cells).

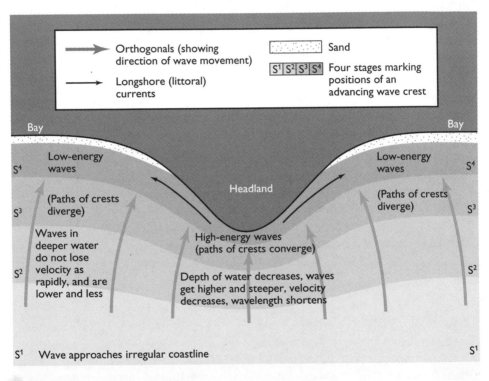

Energy is lost in the formation of the landforms of erosion and deposition, which are covered below.

You need to:

- understand the reasons for wave refraction
- understand the consequences for the coast of this process

Synoptic links

- Unit 1, elements 1 and 2
- Unit 4, element 2

Marine erosional processes and landforms

Processes and types of erosion in coastal areas

Process	Description
Wave pounding	• The mass of water in a wave is very powerful • If a wave breaks at the foot of a cliff or sea wall, shock waves of up to 30 tonnes m^{-2} are generated
Hydraulic pressure	• If air is trapped in a crevice in or between the wave and a cliff or sea wall, the pressure can weaken the cliff or sea wall
Abrasion/ corrasion	• This is the most effective process, especially in storm waves • It is erosion by the load (sand, shingle and boulders) carried in the waves
Attrition	• The load is rounded and made smaller by contact with other particles and the coast
Corrosion/ solution	• This is the chemical reaction of sea water with certain rock types • The carbonation of limestone is important • The growth of salt crystals, which aids the disintegration of rock, can occur up to several metres above high tide • Blue-green algae also contribute to this process; solution carries away the products of this process
Sub-aerial	• These processes are non-marine • They affect the cliffs or coast by means of direct rain action, weathering and mass movement
Human activity	• This includes increased pressure on cliff tops from the weight of buildings, and removal of protective beach material, which increases erosion

Rates of erosion are influenced by a number of factors: the breaking point of the wave; wave steepness; the depth of the sea; the fetch; the nature (shape) of the coastline; the supply of beach material; the width of the beach; rock resistance; rock structure; and rock dip.

Sub-aerial processes are important in coastal areas, as they work with coastal processes to form the coastline. They are covered in more detail in element 2 (geomorphological processes and hazards) of this unit. They include: weathering by processes involving water, temperature and salt; and mass movement, ranging from creep on cliff tops to slumps and landslides on steeper slopes with less resistant rocks, and falls on the steepest ones with more resistant rocks.

You need to:
• be able to define the main processes of coastal erosion

- study the factors that influence the effectiveness of these processes
- know the importance of sub-aerial processes in coastal environments

Synoptic links
- Unit 4, element 2

Coastal erosional landforms

These are best developed on coasts with resistant rocks, but can also be found in areas of less resistant rock. Those named in the specification are bays (and headlands), cliffs, stacks, wave-cut platforms and caves.

Headlands and bays are the product of differential erosion, i.e. the erosion of the weaker rock structures into bays, with the more resistant rocks left as headlands. The process of wave refraction increases erosion on the high-energy headlands, with the more sheltered bays developing beaches in the low-energy environment, which help to protect the shoreline.

Cliffs, stacks, wave-cut platforms and caves are found in areas of resistant rock, frequently in association with each other. The erosive power of the sea is concentrated at tide level and cuts into the coastal material. This will form a cliff where the material can support the steep slope. Continued erosion will form a notch at the base of the cliff which, as it enlarges, will cause the cliff material above to collapse.

The gradient of a cliff depends on a number of factors, including rock type and structure, relief, sub-aerial processes, wave energy and human activity. In many cases, the rock type and structure are very important. Horizontally bedded rocks form vertical cliffs; landward-dipping strata form stable, yet steep cliffs, as particles are not dislodged from the cliff face; and seaward-dipping strata have gradients that follow the dip of the rock as material slides down the plane into the sea.

Thus, the cliff will retreat, leaving a wave-cut platform as it does so, which is exposed at low tide. This platform has a typical angle of 4° and cuts across rock structures. It is marked by abrasion and corrosion, produced by the movement of the tides across the landform. As the cliff retreats, the widening platform dissipates the wave energy and reduces the rate of cliff retreat.

Caves form as marine and/or sub-aerial erosion seeks out a weakness — usually a master-joint or fault in the cliff face. This is eroded over time and is enlarged into a cave or cave system. In limestone areas, caves may be very well developed, as marine and sub-aerial erosion interact effectively. As the cave develops, it may cut back through a headland to form an arch. The collapse of this arch will leave a stack, which is detached from the main cliff. If the stack is worn away, a stump remains. Examples include Flamborough Head, Yorkshire and Old Harry, Swanage.

You need to:
- know the nature and formation of the main landforms of coastal erosion
- be able to give an example of the landforms, including their nature and formation

Sea level changes — causes

Sea level changes are of two types: isostatic and eustatic. These apply to the relative movements of land and sea.

Isostatic changes occur on a regional scale as a result of changes in the Earth's crust. Examples are the sinking of land in a region because of the weight of ice in a glacial period, or the rise of the land after the ice has melted. It can also be a result of tectonics, for example sedimentation in a river delta (causing a decline of land), erosion from mountain chains (causing a rise of land), or volcanic action. Eustatic changes are global sea level changes, caused by the melting or freezing of the ice caps, both as glacial periods come and go and, in more recent times, the possible effects of global warming.

To avoid confusion, a relative rise in sea level is called a positive movement of base level, and a relative fall in sea level is called a negative movement of base level. Base level is the lowest level to which a river can erode.

You need to:
- know the causes of the two types of sea level change
- understand the consequences of positive and negative movements of base level

Sea level changes — the effects on landforms

Changes in base level affect coastal landforms in two ways. A fall in base level causes the existing landforms to be raised above the current sea level and be subjected to sub-aerial erosion. At the same time, new coastal landforms are formed at the new, lower sea level. The landforms exposed include raised beaches and relict cliff lines, which may have other landforms such as caves and wave-cut platforms.

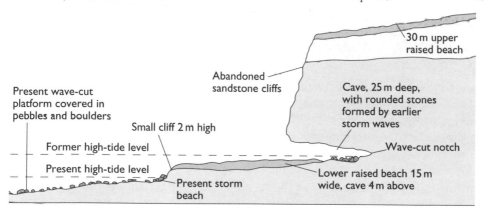

A rise in base level submerges the existing landforms, with new ones forming at the higher sea level. The most spectacular are rias, estuaries and fjords. Rias are the valleys of drowned river uplands, for example in southwest England and Brittany. Estuaries are the valleys of drowned lowland rivers, for example the Thames. Fjords are the valleys of drowned glaciated uplands, for example in Scotland and Norway.

Marine depositional processes and landforms

Coastal deposition — factors and processes

Once sediment has been eroded, it is available for transport by longshore drift. With prevailing winds, such drift will be predominantly in one direction. In southern England, it is predominantly west to east, as the westerlies are the prevailing winds, though the movement in some of the sediment cells is more variable. The material is driven by the waves in a zigzag pattern along the beach. The swash tends to be at an oblique angle up the beach because of wave refraction, but the backwash is at right angles to the beach because of the effects of gravity.

Where longshore drift is slower than the supply of material, the beach will grow, but where longshore drift is faster than the supply of material, the beach will be eroded. People are able to affect the process by building groynes, which cause material to accumulate on the beach, but starve areas of coast downdrift, causing erosion of the beach at that point.

Deposition occurs where the accumulation of sand and shingle exceeds its depletion. This will take place in sheltered areas, or where there is a rapid supply of eroded material. Inputs exceed outputs in this part of the coastal system.

You need to:
- know the process of longshore drift
- understand how this process affects coastal deposition
- be aware of how people can affect this process
- know when and where coastal deposition occurs

Coastal depositional landforms

These landforms are specified as spits/bars, beaches, sand dunes and salt marshes. Spits are long, narrow accumulations of sand and/or shingle. One end is joined to the mainland and the other end projects out to sea or into a river estuary. The formation is a result of longshore drift, which transports beach material along the coast in a straight line into an estuary, with finer sand carried the furthest. Recurved ends are formed by secondary waves in storm conditions approaching from an opposing direction and curving the end, or by normal refraction around the end of the spit. Further growth is impossible because of the speed of the river current and the depth of the water. Wind-blown sand may permit the formation of sand dunes, and salt marsh may form in the sheltered area of water behind the spit where fine mud and silt is deposited. There are many fine examples around the coastline of England and Wales, including Dawlish Warren at the mouth of the River Exe.

Bars are formed in the same way as spits, but they spread across an estuary by longshore drift where the currents are weak, or across a sheltered bay. Alternatively, they can be formed where surging waves push offshore seabed material towards the land. Slapton Ley is a well-known example.

Beaches form where wave energy is dissipated and sediment accumulates faster than it is removed. A beach absorbs the energy of the sea and protects cliffs or land behind. The main landforms found on a beach are shown below.

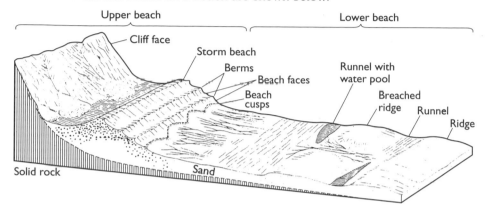

In general, the larger the size of the beach sediment, the steeper is the gradient and the narrower is the beach. Larger-sized material will be pushed to the back of the beach, as the large spaces between particles prevent backwash occurring as strongly as swash. Sandy beaches are therefore less steep and are broader. High-energy spilling (destructive) waves produce wide, flat beaches, whereas low-energy surging (constructive) waves produce narrower, steeper ones. Therefore, beach profiles tend to vary seasonally, as storm waves reduce the gradient in winter and surging waves build it up in the summer.

Sand dunes form where there is a large amount of sand exposed at low tide. This dries out and is blown by onshore winds. When trapped by seaweed or other debris, a series of dunes develops in succession inland, as follows.

Type of dune	Embryo dunes	Fore or yellow dunes	Grey dunes and dune ridges	Wasting dunes with blowouts; dune slacks
Dune height (m)	1	5	8–10	6–8, lower in slacks
% exposed sand	80	20	<10	>40, none in slacks
Humus content	Very little	Some	Increases inland	High
Moisture content	Very little	Very little	Low	High in slacks
pH	>8	>7	6.5–7	5–6
Plant types	Sand couch, lyme grass	Marram, xerophytic species	Creeping fescue, sea spurge, cotton grass, heather; marram dies out	Heather, gorse on dunes, reeds, bog myrtle in slacks

Inland of the wasting or grey dunes, trees may become the dominant form of vegetation.

Salt marshes form in sheltered water in estuaries or behind spits. Here, silt and mud are deposited in the inter-tidal zone, forming mud flats. Algae and *Salicornia* tolerate this long saline submergence and trap more mud around them. *Spartina* grows as the mud develops. Eventually, the mud and vegetation remain above the tide, except in the highest of tides. Hollows may enlarge into virtually unvegetated salt pans. Tide water drains and rises by means of well-developed creek systems, which erode both laterally and vertically.

Environment	Environmental conditions	Plants
Mudflats	High salinity; low oxygen; high turbidity; long periods of tidal inundation	None, only algae
Low marsh	Less hostile, but salinity and turbidity still high and oxygen low; shorter tidal inundation	*Spartina* (cord grass) and *Salicornia* (glasswort) are pioneer species
High marsh	Flooding only in spring tides; low salinity levels; soil develops	Salt marsh grass, sea rush, sea lavender, sea aster, sea blite and sea purslane

You need to:
- know the main landforms of coastal deposition
- understand how these are formed
- give examples of each, at a variety of scales

Sea-level changes — coastal depositional landforms

The effects of submergence have been to create new areas of salt marsh where rivers enter the flooded valleys. Spits, bars, beaches and sand dunes were all submerged, allowing new versions to form where this was possible at the new sea level.

Emergence has caused landforms to be raised above sea level as raised beaches and dune systems. However, if the rise was gradual, the vegetation allowed silt to accumulate as the water rose and the salt marsh was maintained.

You need to:
- know the main impact of sea-level changes on the landforms of coastal deposition
- give examples of depositional landforms at a variety of scales
- be familiar with Cornwall, Dorset, East Anglia and the Baltic Sea as possible cases

Synoptic links
- Unit 1, elements 1 and 3

Coastal problems

Coastal flooding — causes

Coastal flooding is a natural process, but in many cases also has a human influence. One of the main reasons for flooding in coastal areas is the increase in sea level due to either isostatic or eustatic causes. Thus, the relative sinking of southern England for isostatic reasons — as northern Britain rises following the retreat of glaciers — coincides with the eustatic rise in sea level with melting of ice sheets.

The role of global warming in this must be considered, because of the rise in sea level as the land-based ice caps melt and the warming (expansion) of the oceans. The increase in the number and frequency of storms as a consequence of changes in the atmosphere will also increase storm waves and cause more storm surge events.

Human influence too has played a direct part by permitting development on areas liable to flooding. The lack of maintenance of existing coastal defences can also allow flooding to occur.

You need to:
- know that there are both physical and human causes of coastal flooding
- understand that coastal flooding is increasing in frequency and magnitude

> **Synoptic links**
> - Unit 1, element 2

Coastal flooding — consequences and responses

The consequences of flooding are very clear, in that damage occurs to land, crops and property. In the first instance, some coastal environments are able to adapt to a rising sea level. Such areas include salt marsh, mangrove swamps, coral and sand. Damage is greater in areas of coast developed by people. Ports and urban areas are frequently under threat and are unable to adapt in the same way as natural systems.

However, the cost of the damage differs between LEDCs and MEDCs, as does the response to the events. In MEDCs, the response to flooding in coastal areas is to employ both hard and soft engineering strategies in areas of settlement, but to be more flexible on more natural coasts. The take-up of insurance is an additional response.

In LEDCs, the costs of such strategies mean that the response is to live with the risk of flooding. In Bangladesh, for example, where flooding can be caused by high river discharge and/or storm surges, each event causes much loss of life, as well as damage to crops and infrastructure. A rise of 1 metre in sea level would inundate 25% of Bangladesh.

You need to:
- be aware that natural coasts are able to adapt to increasing coastal flooding

- understand that coasts affected by people are unable to adapt
- be familiar with the different responses in LEDCs and MEDCs

Synoptic links
- Unit 4, element 1

Coastal erosion

This is seen in two forms: the loss of land and the slumping of cliffs. Unconsolidated material, as is found on the eastern coast of England, is easily eroded. At Holderness, where the coast consists of glacial till, the rate of retreat is approximately 2 metres each year. Waves of up to 4 metres in height come from the northeast — the maximum fetch. Storm waves comb material down the beach, which is thin and unable to protect the cliffs. The base of the cliffs is undermined, causing them to collapse.

Slumping of cliffs is a product of a number of interrelating factors. The upper part of the slumping occurs, in theory, along a rotational slip plane, which is lubricated by rainwater. The added weight caused by water being held in the pores increases this movement. The base of the cliff is undermined by sea action. The lower part of the slump flows into the sea, from where it is removed by wave action. Hence there are two forms to a slump: the rotation and the flow. The collapse of Holbeck Hall Hotel, near Scarborough, is a well-known, recent reminder of this process.

You need to:
- study the causes and consequences of coastal erosion
- know that land loss and slumping of cliffs are major forms of erosion in areas of less resistant geology

Synoptic links
- Unit 4, element 2
- Unit 5, element 3

Coasts and people — offshore dredging

Impact and response

Offshore dredging has become increasingly common as the demand for sand and gravel for the construction industry has risen. It was originally thought that this would have no effect on the coastal system. However, it was soon discovered that offshore deposits were linked to the beaches and actually supplied material to them. The loss of beach material by longshore drift dredging exposed the land behind the beach to erosion. The best-known example of this occurred at Hallsands in Devon, where the village had to be abandoned after offshore dredging.

The response was to stop dredging. This example caused a reassessment of the activity, and offshore dredging is now subject to licensing and is carefully controlled.

You need to:
- understand the impact of, and responses to, offshore dredging

Coasts and people — sand dunes

Impact and response

Sand dunes are a fragile environment. They are easily disrupted by human influences. The most common impacts are related to the removal of the covering vegetation, by both animals (overgrazing) and people (trampling by tourists).

All sand dune areas are vulnerable to this effect; the main response is to manage the dunes. This can be done by restricting access so that the environment is sustained rather than destroyed. Replanting of vegetation is possible, as is fencing off areas to allow recovery. Selective grazing can also help to protect the natural vegetation. There are many examples of sand dune management in the UK.

You need to:
- understand the impact of, and responses to, sand dune destabilisation

Coasts and people — estuarine environments

Impact and response

People disturb estuarine environments in many ways:
- Flood defences prevent further development of salt marshes
- There may be dredging of channels for navigation
- Land will be used for port and settlement functions
- Water pollution can affect both water and land environments

These areas are under pressure, and although some attempts are made to try to manage and protect them, their economic importance means that success is variable. Estuaries receive the sediment, organic debris and pollutants from river systems. The sediment makes them potentially fertile, but this is offset by the concentration of pollutants, often in the form of heavy metals. As deindustrialisation has taken place in the MEDCs, river estuaries have become much cleaner environments.

You need to:
- know the impact of people on estuarine environments, and the responses

Coasts and people — coral reefs

Impact and response

Coral reefs are ecologically rich environments. Corals are marine animals, which build skeletons of calcium carbonate in which they live. Where they dwell in colonies, in shallow, warm marine environments, they build up coral reefs. They live on organic matter in the sea. Coral reefs are very fragile and are under threat, particularly from pollution and the physical impact of tourists. The sale of coral has increased the pressure on reefs.

The response has been to manage the reefs. Pollution controls and restrictions on tourists have been implemented, as well as controls on reef mining. St Lucia is often quoted as an example of reef management.

You need to:
- be aware of the impact of people on coral reefs, and the responses

Synoptic links
- Unit 1, elements 1, 2 and 3
- Unit 4, element 1

Coastal management strategies

With or against nature?

Management strategies can work either with or against natural processes. Working with nature means allowing the natural processes of erosion to occur (managed retreat), without spending money on the defence of the coast. This policy is usually applied in areas without large settlements. Much of the east coast of England could be in this category. Building coastal defences where deposition is occurring will allow reclamation of land inside the defences.

Working against nature occurs where there is significant human investment on the coast, such as settlements or other valuable land. The cost of defence is justified by the high costs of replacing the human infrastructure. Both hard and soft engineering responses are employed. Hard engineering involves building sea walls, groynes, revetments and flood barriers. Soft engineering includes beach nourishment.

You need to:
- understand that coastal management strategies can be used to work with or against nature
- know that cost–benefit analysis will determine which method is chosen
- be aware that managed retreat works with nature, but hard and soft engineering work against it

Flood protection schemes

These are large-scale projects, involving the construction of dams, barriers, sea walls and dykes. The Dutch Delta Project is suggested in the specification, as well as a comparative project in an LEDC, such as Bangladesh. The scale of the two is affected by the economic development level of the countries.

The Delta Plan in the Netherlands was started some 40 years ago. The plan involved building dams, barriers, sea walls and dykes along the North Sea coast. The Rivers Waal (Rhine), Lek and Maas were controlled as they flowed to the sea. Dykes protected the islands in the delta, and the space between them became fresh water and was used for floodwater overflow. The outer line of sand dunes and the Friesian Islands were joined as an outer barrier against the sea. The global rise in sea level is causing concern, as the defences were not built to accommodate such an event.

In Bangladesh, there is little money to be spent on coastal defences. The policy is to allow the delta area to be inundated, but to defend the capital, Dacca. A flood-wall has been built for this purpose, but has resulted in floodwater being unable to rejoin the river. Flood warnings are provided, but it is difficult for the inhabitants to take full advantage of them, as there is no high land to move to. The economic disruption caused by each flood event contributes to Bangladesh's lack of positive economic development.

You need to:
- know two case studies of flood protection schemes to enable a comparison to be made between an LEDC and an MEDC at a national scale

Coastal protection schemes

These involve the use of groynes, revetments, gabions, sea walls and beach nourishment. The scale is local and normally involves one sediment cell. The Holderness coast and the coast between Hastings and Pett Level are good examples. Care has to be taken to ensure that the scheme does not cause negative downdrift effects, and that the protection of one area of coast does not cause erosion further along the coast. The construction of groynes and the harbour wall at Hastings caused the build up of beach material to protect Hastings itself. This meant that sediment was no longer supplied to the beaches along the coast, especially at Fairlight and Pett Level (to the east). Erosion has taken place at a fast rate, resulting in the removal of beaches and the collapse of the relatively less resistant sands and clays. Housing was under threat at Fairlight.

The response was to build an artificial reef offshore to reduce wave action at the foot of the cliff and to allow beach material to accumulate. This has been very effective, but has increased erosion at Pett Level. Some of this settlement is below sea level on the edge of Romney Marsh and is protected by a sea wall. Groynes and revetments are used to try to hold beach material, and beach nourishment has to be employed to ensure that the sea wall is not eroded. Thus, there is a mixture of hard and soft engineering measures in this example of coastal management.

You need to:
- be able to give an example of coastal management to show a coastal protection scheme at a local scale
- be familiar with the use of hard and soft engineering responses

Coastal management — sand dunes

Sand dunes are an important element in coastal defences, forming an effective barrier against erosion and flooding, and absorbing wave energy. In the Netherlands, the dunes are also a source of fresh water. It is therefore important that they are maintained. The strategies used to protect dunes have been outlined above. Well-known examples in the UK include Morfa Harlech and Ainsdale near Southport. In the Netherlands, beach nourishment has been used to maintain the supply of sand to the dune system.

You need to:
- be aware of the importance of sand dune systems in coastal management
- understand the comparison between the large-scale replenishment scheme in the Netherlands and one small-scale case in the UK

Coastal management — salt marshes

Salt marshes help to protect the coast by absorbing wave energy. They are found in areas with rising sea levels and greater tidal ranges. Many marshes, particularly the high marsh, have been reclaimed from the sea for agricultural or other land uses. Llanriddian Marshes on the Gower Peninsula is a well-known example — the marsh is used for grazing and the collection of shellfish.

You need to:
- understand the importance of salt marsh in coastal management
- be able to give an example of one small-scale case in the UK

Coastal barrages

These are large-scale barriers constructed across bays or estuaries. They are multi-purpose, in that they are intended to keep the fresh water separate from sea water for industrial and domestic use, allow navigation and tourism (yacht marinas), control flooding behind the barrier, and (in some cases) generate HEP by using tidal flows. They are also potential wildlife sanctuaries.

On the other hand, the environmental impact is very great, and often outweighs the potential advantages. The river and coastal flows are affected, with unforeseen consequences in terms of sedimentation. The change of ecology is sudden and irreversible if care is not taken, and the benefits for navigation and tourism may not be a great as expected. The Cardiff Bay Barrier is an example for study.

You need to:
- know the costs and benefits of coastal barrages
- know one case study of a coastal barrier
- understand the values and attitudes that influence the decision-making processes for such schemes

Synoptic links
- Unit 1, element 3
- Unit 2, element 2
- Unit 4, element 1
- Unit 5, elements 1 and 3

Geomorphological processes and hazards

Plate tectonics and landforms

Plate tectonics theory

The theory was developed in the 1960s, but was based on earlier work. Wegener, earlier in the century, saw that the outlines of the continents fitted together, in particular the east coast of America and the west coast of Europe and Africa. He proposed that the continents had moved apart under continental drift, but was unable to offer a mechanism for this.

In the 1960s and 1970s, seabed research showed that the pattern of magnetic orientation of iron particles in rocks was the same on either side of the mid-ocean ridges, particularly in the Atlantic. Study of the rocks showed that the sea floor was spreading from the ridges at a consistent rate on each side. Both pieces of evidence suggested the sea floor was spreading from these ridges as it was being created.

This led to the development of the theory that the Earth's crust is made up of rigid plates. These are moved by convection currents in the mantle, and the movement causes the creation of the plates at the mid-oceanic ridges and their destruction at the destructive margins. Plates are either oceanic or continental, depending on the type of crustal material.

You need to:
- know the origins of the theory of continental drift
- understand the development of plate tectonics theory
- give an example of the evidence for plate movement

Types of plate margin

There are three main types of plate margin: destructive, constructive and conservative. They offer an explanation for the occurrence of ocean ridges, deep-sea trenches and island arcs, and a very large proportion of earthquakes, volcanoes, fold mountains, faults and rift valleys.

Constructive plate margin

Processes

Oceanic crust is created at the site of upwelling currents in the mantle. The new crust then moves away in opposite directions, allowing new magma to rise to fill the space and cool, creating more new crust. This, in turn, is moved on the mantle current to the destructive margin.

Landforms

Very active volcanoes form, with frequent eruptions of free-flowing, less explosive, basic lava. The vulcanism causes the mid-ocean ridges to build up as submarine mountains, which reach the sea surface as islands. There is a distinct rift valley in the ridge, indicating where the crust is spreading. Transform faulting also results in the ridge being split into blocks along its length. Earthquakes are frequent and less powerful than at destructive margins, occurring along the ridge and the transform faults, usually at shallow depths. An example is the mid-Atlantic ridge forming the Eurasian and North American plates.

Destructive plate margin

Processes

The oceanic crust created at the constructive margin is destroyed. The mantle currents descend and the oceanic crust is subducted into the mantle.

Landforms

These depend on the type of plate under which the oceanic crust is subducted.

Oceanic–oceanic destructive plate margin

At destructive oceanic margins, where both plates are composed of oceanic crust, the active plate is subducted under the passive, causing the formation of deep-sea trenches. Island arcs form at some distance beyond the plate in the form of a line of volcanoes roughly parallel to the trench, where less dense material rises as it melts under the process of subduction. These volcanoes can be very explosive, as crustal material is mixed into the subducted material, but they may not always be so. Eruptions tend to be relatively frequent. Earthquakes tend to be frequent, less powerful than when continental crust is involved, and shallow, but can be very powerful when associated with volcanic eruptions. An example is the Philippines, where the Pacific plate meets the Philippines plate.

Oceanic–continental destructive plate margin

Oceanic crust is subducted beneath the continental plate because the continental crustal material is less dense. An oceanic trench is formed, but the subduction causes magma to rise up through and melt the continental crust. The volcanic activity which results varies in its intensity, both spatially and temporally, but it is usually explosive because the material is more acidic and more viscous. Earthquakes are deeper and frequently more powerful than at constructive margins. The opposing movement of the plates causes the formation of fold mountain chains on the continental plate, as the sediments deposited in the marginal geosyncline by erosion of continental material are folded and faulted and raised above sea level. An example is the Andes, where the South American plate meets the Nazca plate.

Continental–continental destructive plate margin

At destructive continental margins, two continental plates meet. As the two plates move towards each other, subduction occurs at an early stage. This allows the formation of an oceanic trench, some volcanic activity and the formation of fold mountains, as well as the occurrence of powerful earthquakes. However, as the process continues, the two continental crusts meet. As they are both of low density, subduction cannot occur and the plates appear to become wedged. The process of subduction ceases and only earthquake activity and mountain building continue. An example is the Himalayas, where the Indo-Australian plate meets the Eurasian plate.

The relationship between constructive and destructive plates is shown in the diagram below.

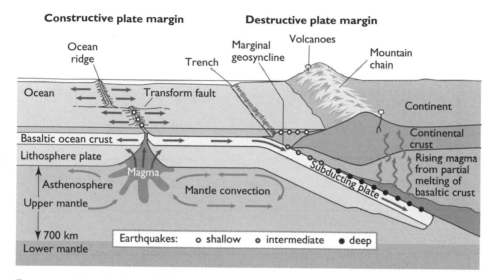

Constructive plate margin   **Destructive plate margin**

Conservative plate margin
Processes
The two plates move past each other in the same relative direction, so that no subduction occurs.

Landforms
There is no volcanic activity at these margins, but earthquakes are frequent and can be very powerful. The area of the margin has a great number of major and minor faults and the potential for activity is very great. Rift valleys and block mountains are common because of the great stresses affecting the crust. An example is the San Andreas Fault in California, where the North American plate and the Pacific plate are juxtaposed.

You need to:
- know that there are three main types of plate margin
- understand that these margins help to explain the occurrence of a variety of landforms
- be aware that each margin has its own associated landforms

Hot spots

There is one type of volcanic activity which is not associated with plate margins: hot spots. These are considered to be the result of hot plumes of magma in the mantle rising through the oceanic crust and causing magma to reach the surface as volcanoes. The Hawaiian Islands are a good example. They are aligned from north-west to southeast, with the active volcanoes to the southeast. The movement of the Pacific plate has been from southeast to northwest over time, so the oldest volca-noes, to the northwest, have passed over the plume and are now extinct. The seamounts, as they are called, are very large, rising from the ocean floor to well above sea level. They have sides of gentle gradient, as the magma is basic.

You need to:
- understand that some volcanic activity is not associated with plate margins
- know that hot spots are the result of rising magma in the mantle forming seamounts
- be aware that movement of the oceanic plate causes the seamounts to become extinct as they pass over and away from the plume

Volcanic activity

Eruptions

There are variations in the form, frequency and type of volcanic eruptions. These are related to the types of plate margin, emissions, vents and lava. The emissions can be solid, gaseous and/or liquid. The relationship with plate margins has been outlined above. The two main types of lava, basic and acidic (though there is a great variety between the extremes), are defined by the amount of silica they contain — basic having a low proportion (around 50%) and acidic having a high proportion (about 66%). This affects the mineral content, the gas content and the viscosity of the lava.

Basic lava is at a higher temperature (1200 °C), loses gases more slowly (so is less explosive) and is relatively free-flowing. Eruptions are gentle but more frequent, producing more gently sloping landforms. Lava and steam are the main materials ejected.

In contrast, acidic lava is at a lower temperature (800 °C), loses gases more quickly (so is more explosive) and is more viscous. Eruptions are less frequent, and landforms have steeper slopes. Ash, rocks, gases, cinders, steam and lava are ejected.

You need to:
- understand that volcanic emissions can be solids, gases and/or liquids
- know that there are two main types of lava
- be aware that their characteristics offer explanations for the types of eruption

Intrusive and extrusive landforms

Volcanic landforms are classified into two broad categories. Intrusive landforms are those formed by volcanic activity within the Earth's crust, whereas extrusive are those formed by volcanic activity on the surface.

Intrusive volcanic landforms
These are formed within the crust, but are then exposed by the erosion of the overlying

rocks. The slowly cooling magma allows large mineral crystals to form and the rock splits into large joints. The main landforms are batholiths, laccoliths, sills and dykes.

Batholiths are the largest intrusions, comprising upwelling magma from the subduction zones. They are usually granite, frequently domed and several hundred kilometres in cross section. Around the batholith is a metamorphic aureole, where the heat and pressure alter the surrounding rocks and allow valuable minerals to be injected. An example is Dartmoor, southwest England. Smaller batholiths are called bosses.

Laccoliths are intrusive landforms formed by magma intruding into horizontal strata, and then doming on the upper side, for example the Black Cuillins of Skye, Scotland.

Dykes are narrow vertical intrusions of magma that cut across the bedding planes of sedimentary rocks. They frequently occur in swarms in a small area and may surround a boss to form ring dykes. They are frequently more resistant than the surrounding rocks, for example Arran, Scotland.

Sills are horizontal intrusions along the bedding planes of the surrounding sedimentary rocks. They form a layer of rock up to several hundred metres thick. This forms a distinctive jointed feature when exposed after erosion, for example Great Whin Sill, northern England.

Extrusive volcanic landforms

The main volcanic landforms are volcanoes, but they also include lava plateaux, geysers, hot springs/boiling mud and solfataras. They form rocks with small crystals as they cool rapidly at the surface. These include basalt and pyroclastic material from volcanoes.

Volcanoes can be classified by the shape of the volcano, the material ejected and the vent. The main types are as follows:

- **Fissure eruptions** consist of a central vent where two plates or a fault move apart. The lava is basic, usually basalt, which flows freely over long distances. Repeated eruptions can build up into large lava plateaux, for example Giant's Causeway, Co. Antrim or the Deccan, India.
- **Shield volcanoes** occur where basic lava flows from a central vent, spreading over large areas. The volcano is gently-sided, made up of many lava flows, for example Mauna Loa, Hawaii.
- **Acid/dome volcanoes** are steep-sided convex cones, consisting of viscous lava that solidifies near the crater, for example Mount Pelée, Martinique.
- **Ash and cinder cones** are formed from pyroclastic ash cinders and bombs ejected from the crater. The sides are steep and symmetrical, but the landforms are small because they are easily eroded, for example Paracutin, Mexico.
- **Composite cones** are the most common volcanoes, made up of layers of ash and lava. Ash is associated with explosive phases, while lava results in more gentle eruptions, for example Etna, Sicily.
- **Calderas** are a result of the build-up of gases, when violent explosions blast from the magma chamber in the volcano and remove the summit. The sides of the crater

subside, widening the opening to several kilometres. They are frequently flooded by the sea, for example Krakatoa, Indonesia.

Gases and liquids are also emitted from volcanoes, and can be divided as follows:

- **Geysers** occur when water is heated in the crust to become superheated steam underground. Pressure builds up, causing the water and steam near the surface to be ejected, for example Old Faithful, Yellowstone National Park.
- **Hot springs/boiling mud** consist of water which is heated in the crust, but does not eject violently, merely spilling onto the surface. When this mixes with mud, boiling mud is formed, for example Bath, UK.
- **Solfataras** occur when volcanic gases, especially sulphur, are ejected into the air at the surface, for example Etna, Sicily.

You need to:

- be familiar with the main classification of volcanic activity into extrusive and intrusive landforms
- know the main types of intrusive volcanic landforms
- be able to describe examples from the UK, where possible, of intrusive landforms. For example, Edinburgh has a volcanic plug (Castle Rock) and a sill (Arthur's Seat).
- know the main types of extrusive volcanic landforms
- be able to show examples from the UK, where possible, of extrusive landforms. These include hot springs (Bath) and a volcanic plug (Edinburgh).

Synoptic links
- Unit 5, element 3

Earthquakes

Characteristics

An earthquake is the product of tension in the crust. This tension is released in the form of an earthquake as the movement of the rocks on a fault line releases energy in the form of waves. The point within the crust where the earthquake occurs is the focus, and the point directly above the focus on the surface is the epicentre.

The study of earthquakes is called seismology — earthquakes are measured using a seismograph. There are three main types of wave: P, S and L waves.

Primary (P) waves displace particles horizontally as they move from the focus/epicentre, and are the fastest waves. Secondary (S) waves displace particles at right angles to the direction of movement away from the focus/epicentre. They travel at three-fifths of the velocity of P waves. L waves move along the surface.

P waves pass through both solids and liquids, so will pass through the mantle and the core. They are refracted as they do so, leaving a shadow zone where no P waves are recorded. S waves will not pass through liquids and so do not pass through the core, producing a large shadow zone. This enables the focus of an earthquake to be precisely located. L waves travel the slowest, but produce the greatest effects on structure. The greatest effects are near to the epicentre.

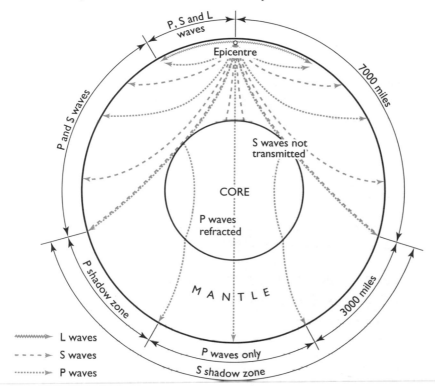

You need to:

- understand the distinction between the focus and the epicentre
- know the main types of earthquake wave

Measurement of earthquake energy

The Richter scale measures earthquake energy. It is a logarithmic scale, so each whole number increases by a factor of ten. For example, an earthquake measuring 4 on the scale has ten times more energy than one of 3, and 100 times more energy than one of 2. The strongest earthquakes have been recorded at between 9 and 10 on the scale.

You need to:

- be aware that earthquake energy is measured on the Richter scale
- know that it is a logarithmic scale

Earthquakes — land and sea distribution

As explained earlier, earthquakes are found in concentrations along the three main types of plate margin: constructive, destructive and conservative. Because the latter two types are on or close to land, the earthquakes with the greatest impact on people are associated with these margins. Earthquakes are associated not only with faulting near plate margins, but also with faults that are found away from plate margins. These tend to be less powerful, but occur in areas not as readily associated with earthquakes. Earthquakes in the UK fall into this category, for example Colchester (1884) and Lleyn Peninsula, Wales (1985).

Tsunamis are waves caused by submarine earthquakes. These are associated with plate margins and other major faults. The shock waves travel through the water and rise steeply as the shore is reached to form a wave or tidal surge that can be tens of metres high. Much damage is inflicted on coastal areas, as happened in Alaska (1964), where a tsunami caused great devastation on the surrounding islands and the mainland, though these areas were not heavily populated.

You need to:
- be able to explain that the distribution of earthquakes is related to the distribution of plate margins
- understand that other, less powerful earthquakes occur on fault lines away from plate margins
- know that tsunamis occur as a result of submarine earthquakes

Earthquakes — human involvement

Human activity, for example explosions or dam building, can also trigger earthquakes. In the case of dams, faults and similar weaknesses can be lubricated by water seeping into the bedrock. This triggers a number of small, but frequently occurring, earthquakes. The sheer weight of water in the lake behind the dam can also produce similar effects in the underlying rocks.

You need to:
- understand that people can contribute to the occurrence of earthquakes
- study a range of earthquakes, their consequences and human responses to them, from the small scale to the global
- keep a record of major earthquakes as they occur during your course (there will almost certainly be at least one). Two cases should be sufficient

Synoptic links
- Unit 2, element 3
- Unit 4, element 2

Weathering and mass movement

Weathering — definitions

Weathering is the natural breakdown of rocks in situ (in their original position). It is distinguished from erosion, in that there is no movement of material. The weathered layer of material on the surface is known as the regolith.

There are two main types of weathering: mechanical (physical) and chemical. However, in reality, both often work together. The specification also refers to biological weathering, which is the action of plants on rocks, which many see as a subset of mechanical weathering.

You need to:

- know the difference between weathering and erosion
- be able to list the main types of weathering

Types of weathering — mechanical

Name of process	Process	Products
Frost shattering	• This is most common where temperatures fluctuate around freezing point • Water freezes in joints, cracks, pores and bedding planes at night, and melts during the day • Ice forms, and the water expands by 9% as it freezes • This exerts pressure on the rock and, over time, the continuous freeze–thaw action causes it to disintegrate	• Shattered angular rock, block disintegration in jointed rock, and sand particles • Collection of large blocks at the foot of steep slopes are known as scree and, on more gentle slopes, are blockfields
Salt crystallisation	• Where water is saline, salt crystals (rather than ice) form • The growth of crystals causes stress, resulting in disintegration • The process tends to occur in arid and semi-arid climates, and on coasts	• Sand, as the process mostly occurs in the pores of sandstone
Pressure release	• Rocks form under great pressure in the crust • As they reach the surface, the pressure is released and joints and bedding planes appear	• Sheeting — rocks crack parallel to the surface • Exfoliation domes on large exposures of rock
Thermal expansion or exfoliation	• Alternate heating and cooling cause stress, so that the outer layers of rock peel off • This is now seen as partly a chemical action, as temperature changes do not show this effect without the presence of water • Differential heating and cooling of minerals causes the break-up of the rock as each crystal/particle expands and contracts at a different rate	• Granular disintegration in sandstones and granites
Biological weathering	• Plant roots are able to open joints and other weaknesses in rocks • Burrowing animals play a similar role	• Block disintegration in jointed rocks • The break-up of sandstone into sand

You need to:
- be familiar with the main types of mechanical weathering
- be able to explain the processes by which they operate
- know the products of the processes

Types of weathering — chemical

Name of process	Process	Products
Oxidation	• The reaction of minerals with exposure to oxygen • The change from a ferric to ferrous compound, or from a blue-grey to a red-brown (rust) colour	• The disintegration of sedimentary rocks with iron as the cement, frequently forming sand
(Reduction)	• (This is the reverse of oxidation, and occurs in waterlogged areas)	
Hydration	• The absorption of water by certain minerals, causing swelling and physical disintegration, as well as chemical disintegration	• Anhydrite changes to gypsum • Also important in forming clay particles
Hydrolysis	• The reaction of hydrogen in water with minerals • The greater the number of H^+ ions, the greater is the reaction	• Very important in formation of clays • Feldspar in granite breaks down into kaolinite (china clay) • Mica releases aluminium and iron in more acidic conditions
Carbonation	• The reaction of limestone with rainwater (carbonic acid) • The limestone changes from calcium carbonate (insoluble) to calcium bicarbonate (soluble) and is removed in solution	• Weathering of limestone, forming distinctive landforms • Disintegration of rocks with lime cements into sands
Solution	• The removal of other weathered minerals in solution	• Rock salt and calcium bicarbonate removed
Biological	• The weathering caused by humic acids • Organic activity increases CO_2 content and thus carbonation • Acid rain, the product of increased CO_2, SO_2 and NO in solution in the atmosphere	• Increased chemical weathering, but reduced mechanical weathering, under vegetation • Increased weathering of limestone and sandstone by carbonation and hydrolysis

You need to:

- know the main types of chemical weathering
- understand the processes by which they operate
- be aware of the products of these processes

Weathering — rates of activity

Weathering is influenced by a number of factors. The rate of weathering depends on the structure and mineral composition of the rock, the climate, vegetation cover and time. Rock type and vegetation are mentioned in the tables above, while the role of climate is summarised in the diagram below.

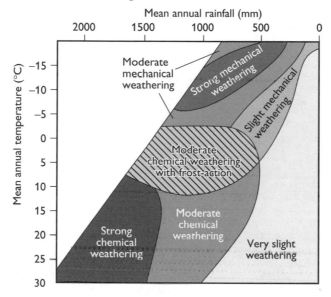

In general, mechanical weathering is more important where temperatures fluctuate around freezing point. Chemical weathering increases in hotter and wetter areas, and where there is greater humic activity. The rate of chemical weathering doubles with every 10 °C increase in temperature, but carbonation is very effective at just above freezing point.

You need to:

- understand the factors that affect the rate of weathering
- be able to explain the role of climate in these rates

Weathering — the role of people

People have a number of influences on weathering and are, in turn, affected by it. The main influences of people on both mechanical and chemical weathering have been outlined above. The main impact on people comes in a number of forms. The increased weathering of building stone and, on a smaller scale, gravestones, is well documented. In particular, chemical weathering increased following the Industrial

Revolution, due to the higher concentrations of sulphur dioxide and oxides of nitrogen in urban areas. This resulted in the severe weathering of, in particular, limestone and marble. The costs of cleaning and replacing the stone in such buildings as St Paul's Cathedral in central London and the Sheldonian Theatre in Oxford, both built of Portland stone, were very great. There have been recent improvements in air quality.

You need to:
- be aware of the involvement of people in weathering
- be able to explain the impact of weathering on people, especially in the urban environment

Mass movement — definition and types

Mass movement is the downhill movement of all weathered material under the influence of gravity. Gravity and the amount of water present influence the processes. Movements are classified as heave, flow and slide.

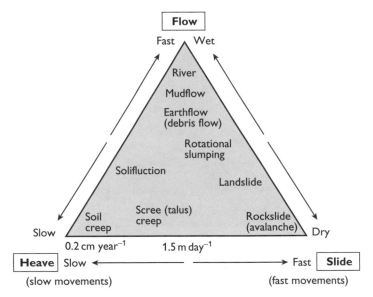

You need to:
- be able to give a definition of mass movement
- understand the factors influencing these movements
- know the main types of movement

Mass movement — heave

Soil creep is the main heave process. It is the slowest movement, at less than 1 cm year^{-1}, and usually occurs continuously on gentle, vegetated slopes. Freeze–thaw, heating–cooling and wetting–drying cause the downslope movements. In freeze–thaw, the growth of ice crystals causes the soil to expand and lift particles at right angles to the slope (heave). When the ice melts, the particles fall vertically, thus moving imperceptibly downhill. Wetting causes the soil to expand and to move downslope under gravity. In dry periods, the drying of the soil causes it to contract downslope under gravity. When heated, particles expand downslope, but when contracting, cannot move back to the original position because of gravity.

The main signs of creep include piled up soil upslope and loss of soil downslope of walls and trees, as well as leaning trees and telegraph poles, and tension gashes in roads and fields (terracettes are caused in this way). Creep is also involved in the formation of stone polygons and stone stripes in periglacial areas (see p. 60).

You need to:
- understand the conditions under which creep occurs
- be able to explain the processes by which creep occurs
- know the landforms produced by the processes

Mass movement — flow

Flow moves with internal deformation as the base is slowed by friction and the upper material falls to the front of the moving body of material.

Solifluction is the process by which soil flows downhill in periglacial or similar areas. The active layer on the surface is frozen in winter, but in summer it thaws. The permafrost below acts as an impermeable layer and the saturated topsoil flows gently downslope, often only 50–100 cm each year. The main landforms include solifluction lobes and head — a layer of solifluction material in valleys and at the foot of cliffs in southern UK. This is a remnant of the last ice advance.

Earthflow occurs when the regolith on steeper slopes becomes saturated and slowly flows. Velocity can be from 1 to 15 km per year. The vegetation may not be broken, and the main landform is a small lobe with perhaps short flow tracks.

Mudflow is a much more rapid movement, usually over $1 \, \text{km h}^{-1}$, but has been recorded at $40 \, \text{km h}^{-1}$. The regolith becomes saturated very quickly, either by heavy rainfall or by rapidly melting ice during a volcanic eruption. This, with the increase in weight, destabilises the slope. Mudflows are characterised by a rounded scar at the start, a flowtrack, and a lobe or debris fan where the material is finally deposited.

You need to:
- know the different types of flow
- be able to explain the conditions under which flow occurs
- understand the processes by which flow occurs
- study the landforms produced by the processes

Mass movement — slide

Slide has no internal deformation, i.e. it moves as one mass along a slip plane. Slide is frequent where bedding planes are parallel to the angle of slope. This is likely to be a planar slide, leaving a rupture surface.

A rotational slide, or slump, produces an upper rotational slip plane, with a lobe of flowed material that has been deposited at the base. The slip plane is usually lubricated by rainfall. In addition, the increased weight of water in the saturated material increases the risk of sudden movement. Undermining at the base of the slope by the sea or a river is also important in triggering these distinctive landforms which are common on the eastern and southern coasts of England.

An avalanche can be of two types: rock or snow. Rock avalanches occur on steep slopes, resulting in the movement of dry material downslope. Snow avalanches are usually triggered by a rise in temperature, causing the upper layers of snow to move over the frozen material below. Both cause a substantial amount of damage in mountainous areas.

Falls occur on very steep slopes, over $40°$. They may result from weathering of bare rock, undermining by the sea, or earthquake shock waves. The material falls to the base of the slope, where it will be removed by sea, river or ice, or remain as scree.

You need to:
- know the different types of slide
- be able to explain the conditions under which slide occurs
- understand the processes by which slide occurs
- be familiar with the landforms produced by the processes
- explore the relationships between weathering, mass movement and erosion
- be able to give small-scale examples

Synoptic links
- Unit 1, elements 1, 2 and 3
- Unit 4, elements 1 and 3

The impact of, and response to, geomorphological processes and hazards

Impact on the natural world

Geomorphological processes and hazards have a major impact on the natural world, particularly in the short term. In the long term, systems are self-regulating.

Volcanic activity, earthquakes, weathering and mass movement all have strong effects on ecosystems and plant succession. The vegetation is often completely destroyed in areas affected by a volcanic eruption. Succession is then interrupted, and unless there are further eruptions, restarts as secondary succession. Alternatively, this can be seen as a prisere (lithosere). This theme is covered in Module 1.

The impact of major mass movement events on ecosystems is equally devastating, but the vegetation is able to re-establish itself in a few years, given stability of the slope. This too can be viewed as either secondary succession or a prisere (lithosere).

You need to:
- be aware of the impact of geomorphological processes and hazards on ecosystems and ecological succession

Impact on human activity

The definition of a hazard indicates that it is detrimental to people or property. The perception of a hazard will vary according to the degree of impact that it has on people, the level of economic development and the resources the people are prepared to commit to adjusting to it. The impact can be recognised in terms of prediction of the hazard, modification of the hazard, reduction of vulnerability of the people, adaptation to the hazard and recovery from the hazard event. This is explored below.

Vulcanicity

	MEDC (expenditure more likely)	LEDC (expenditure less likely)
Prediction	• Possible in short term • Research • Monitoring	• Possible • Research • Monitoring
Modification	• Divert lava flows	• Unlikely
Reduction in vulnerability	• Avoidance of high-risk areas • Evacuation plans and resources • Insurance	• Ignore risk • Avoidance, but other pressures often negate this • Evacuate at first signs or after eruption
Adaptation	• Avoidance of high-risk areas • Use resources provided by volcano — soils, minerals, tourism and energy	• Use resources provided by volcano — soils, minerals etc.
Recovery	• Disaster plans carried out • State funding for recovery • Insurance payouts	• Very limited • NGO and external aid provided in relatively small amounts

Earthquakes

	MEDC (expenditure more likely)	LEDC (expenditure less likely)
Prediction	• Not possible • Research • Monitoring	• Not possible • Research • Monitoring
Modification	• Not usually possible • Lubrication of slip planes	• Unlikely

	MEDC (expenditure more likely)	LEDC (expenditure less likely)
Reduction in vulnerability	• Avoidance of high-risk areas • Emergency plans and resources • Insurance • Reduce impact of waves by adaptation	• Ignore risk • Avoidance, but other pressures often negate this
Adaptation	• Avoidance of high-risk areas • Adapt buildings and other infrastructure	• Avoidance of high-risk areas • Try to survive after event
Recovery	• Emergency/disaster plans carried out • State funding for recovery • Insurance payouts	• Very limited • NGO and external aid provided in relatively small amounts • Risk of disease, food and water shortages greater

Mass movement

	MEDC (expenditure more likely)	LEDC (expenditure less likely)
Prediction	• Possible by identification of high-risk areas and weather conditions • Research • Monitoring	• Possible, but not often acted upon
Modification	• Drainage of slip planes in areas likely to slump or slide • Creation of avalanche runs, fences and tunnels • Coastal defences	• Unlikely
Reduction in vulnerability	• Avoidance of high-risk areas • Ignore small-scale movements • Emergency plans and resources • Insurance • Coastal defences	• Ignore risk • Avoidance, but other pressures often negate this
Adaptation	• Avoidance of high-risk areas • Drainage • Creation of avalanche runs, fences and tunnels	• Avoidance of high-risk areas • Survival after event
Recovery	• Emergency/disaster plans carried out • State funding for recovery (if on large scale) • Insurance payouts	• Very limited • NGO and external aid provided in relatively small amounts • Risk of disease, food and water shortages greater

The provision of emergency aid in response to such events also emphasises the concept of interdependence between the MEDW and the LEDW — most of the aid will come from the MEDW, from both governments and non-governmental organisations

(NGOs). You will be able to explore your own attitudes and values to such events as they occur and as you study them.

You should bear in mind that the event itself (primary effect), although hazardous, has a greater impact on property than on people. The secondary effects following the event, such as disease, water and food shortages, lack of shelter and fire (after earthquakes), tend to cause more harm to people than the event itself. Please note that when studying earthquakes, the primary and secondary effects of the event should not be confused with the primary and secondary waves.

You need to:

- understand the impact of hazards on human activity
- be aware of the varying perceptions and responses to such events
- be familiar with the adjustments made by people in the face of the hazard, to include prediction, modification, reduction in vulnerability, adaptation and recovery
- understand the importance of global interdependence in the responses to the hazards
- consider your attitudes and values towards such events
- give examples of case studies on a regional or national scale, to show the MEDC and LEDC contrasts
- know the positive elements of hazards, particularly those arising from vulcanicity

Synoptic links
- Unit 1, elements 2 and 3
- Unit 2, elements 1 and 3
- Unit 4, element 1
- Unit 5, element 3

Cold environments and human activity

The environment

Cold environments — definitions

The study area corresponds to:

- the polar regions — especially the tundra biome and the ice-cap regions polewards, including the surrounding seas (this includes northern Alaska, Canada, Scandinavia and Russia)
- Antarctica, including the Southern Ocean
- alpine environments — those above the tree line in temperate areas (this includes the Alps in Europe, parts of the Western Cordillera (USA and Canada) and parts of the Himalayas)

There are three climatic areas identified: tundra, polar and temperate montane. Typical climatic characteristics for a tundra area are shown below.

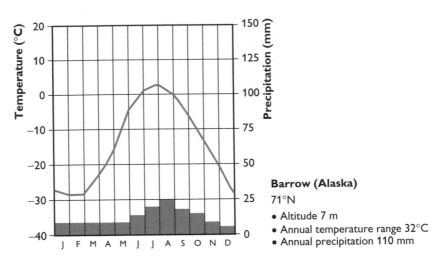

Barrow (Alaska)
71°N
• Altitude 7 m
• Annual temperature range 32°C
• Annual precipitation 110 mm

The characteristics are that mean temperatures remain below freezing for most of the year and only rise to about 3 °C in the 2 months or so that they are above freezing, allowing the active layer to be formed. The growing season, which lasts for approximately 60 days, is therefore exceptionally short. There is a large annual temperature range of 31°C. The prevailing winds are polar easterlies, blowing from the polar high pressure cells. These give clear skies for much of the year. In winter, the temperatures fall to –28 °C when the ground is frozen, and there are 6–10 months of continuous night. Precipitation is low, at 110 mm year^{-1} in Barrow, and falls mostly as blizzard snow. There is a summer maximum. This is a cold desert area.

In the continental interiors, the maritime influence is lost and temperatures are lower all year, but precipitation is also lower. Coastal and island areas open to warmer ocean currents have a more moderate climate as the sea remains unfrozen. For example, Spitsbergen (78 °N) has a February mean of –1 °C and higher precipitation as mid-latitude depressions pass into the polar zones.

Closer to the poles, the polar climate is one of perpetual frost. Air temperatures are higher in summer but remain below freezing. Blizzards are frequent in winter.

Alpine areas are found in the Alps and other mountain ranges of central and northern Europe, including upland Britain. Other areas include the Himalayas and the Rocky Mountains of North America. Altitude reduces temperatures to below freezing in winter to create a tundra-type environment, but in summer, temperatures may be higher. Precipitation also tends to be higher than in the classic tundra, as the mid-latitude depressions affect these areas, and the mountain ranges are so large that they create their own climates. The altitude at which these areas are found increases towards the tropics, for example 1000 m in Scotland, 1500 m in Alaska, 2000 m in the Alps and 3500 m in Colorado and the western Himalayas.

You need to:

- know the areas of cold climates
- explore the characteristics of the climates, including some variations
- understand the reasons for the climatic characteristics

Cold climates — hazards

Intense cold, wind chill and low precipitation are the main hazards for people in these areas. The high latitudes cause intense cold, with little solar radiation received. The summers are short, with temperatures just above freezing. In the winter, the hours of daylight are very short. In polar areas, temperatures are below freezing all year round. The high pressure that dominates, causes cloudless skies, thus allowing any solar radiation received in the day to be radiated out at night.

Wind chill has a very strong effect. Wind chill is the additional loss of heat experienced because of the force of the wind. For example, a wind speed of $8\,km\,h^{-1}$ at $-1\,°C$ will be experienced as a temperature of $-3\,°C$, whereas a wind speed of $48\,km\,h^{-1}$ at the same temperature will be experienced as one of $-10\,°C$. Winds are frequently strong in all tundra areas, especially in blizzards, and many areas have featureless plains with no obstacles to break the wind. Winds are similarly high in alpine areas. These conditions are very difficult for people to live in without adequate protection.

Low precipitation would normally mean that agriculture is impossible, trees cannot grow and there is insufficient water for people to live in these desert areas. However, the low temperatures, short summer, strong winds and frozen ground, with thaw in the summer months, mean that these activities are impossible anyway.

You need to:

- know the hazards of cold, wind and low precipitation
- be able to explain the reasons for these hazards
- understand how these hazards affect people

Synoptic links

- Unit 1, element 2

Glacial and periglacial processes and landforms

Landscape processes — weathering and mass movement

You are able to study areas which are currently affected by these processes and those that have experienced them in the geologically recent past. The weathering and mass movement processes operating in these areas have been mentioned above. The weathering processes are those that operate where temperatures fluctuate around freezing point, bearing in mind that no processes operate when temperatures are below freezing. Frost shattering is the most obvious, but pressure release and chemical action (reflecting the greater concentration of carbon dioxide in snow) also occur. Mass movement includes movements at all speeds, with the role of water limited to thaw conditions. Thus, solifluction is important in periglacial areas, but heave movements are also significant. Slides occur in the form of avalanches in mountainous regions, especially in alpine areas, and falls of shattered material are common on steep slopes.

You need to:
- know how weathering and mass movement operate in cold environments

Landscape processes — glacial erosion, transport and deposition

The processes of glacial erosion are abrasion, plucking, rotational movement and extending and compressing flow. Abrasion involves the use of material produced by frost shattering to erode the valley sides and base. Plucking involves ice pulling away weathered material by freezing onto rock surfaces. It is most effective when temperatures fluctuate around freezing point and water is available for freezing. This is likely either when pressure-point melting causes ice to melt and allows freeze–thaw to break the ice–rock contact, or when water flows into the ice via crevasses.

Pressure release also aids the plucking process. Rotational movement occurs in cirques and overdeepens the landform as the rotation increases pressure on its floor. Variations in ice velocity cause increased erosion where flow is extending (greater velocity) and less where it is compressive (lower velocity).

Glaciers transport large amounts of material, known as moraine. Supraglacial moraine is transported as lateral and medial moraine; englacial moraine is transported within the glacier; and subglacial moraine is transported on the valley floor. Fluvial transport also occurs in the same locations, as meltwater flows over the surface, within the ice and along the base, subject to temperature conditions. The material transported will be sand and gravel, as it will be sorted by the flowing water.

Glaciers deposit their load in two forms, one being glacial till (moraine), which is deposited directly by the ice and will be unsorted and inside the ice margin. Fluvioglacial material, the second form, is deposited by meltwater streams, both within and outside the ice margin, and is sorted. Deposition occurs both in upland valleys and on lowland plains.

You need to:
- know the processes of glacial erosion
- be familiar with the factors that affect rates of erosion
- understand the processes of glacial transport, by both ice and water
- understand the processes of glacial deposition, again by ice and water
- be able to name the materials of erosion, transport and deposition

The glacial budget

A glacier is a system; it has inputs (snow, falling directly or by avalanches), stores (ice and meltwater) and transfers and outputs (meltwater, evaporation and icebergs).

The upper part of the glacier is the zone of accumulation, where inputs exceed outputs. The lower part is the zone of ablation, where outputs exceed inputs. The zone of equilibrium is where the rates of accumulation and ablation are in balance. The glacier budget is the difference between the total accumulation and total ablation for the year. In temperate glaciers (see below), the balance is likely to be negative in summer and positive in winter. Where the budget is positive, the ice snout will be advancing, but where it is negative, the snout will be retreating. When the budget is in balance, the snout will appear to be stationary.

You need to:
- understand that the glacier is a system with inputs, stores, transfers and outputs
- know the glacial budget and its components
- be able to explain the effect of the glacial budget on the glacier snout

Warm and cold glaciers

There are two types of glacier: warm and cold. The characteristics of each affect the movement and operation of glacial processes.

Warm ice has a temperature of about 0 °C throughout its mass. It has large amounts of meltwater available. Glaciers of this type are temperate glaciers, and their movement is faster as the water lubricates the ice, reducing friction. The movement can be by basal flow, creep, extending and compressing flow and surges. This type of glacier is more likely to erode, transport and deposit material.

Cold ice has temperatures permanently below 0 °C throughout its mass and hence there is no meltwater. Glaciers of this type are polar glaciers. Movement is slower, because they tend to be frozen to their beds, moving mainly by internal flow. Less erosion, transport and deposition occur.

Both types of ice may be found at different points of a glacier's profile.

You need to:
- know the characteristics of warm and cold glaciers
- understand the effects these characteristics have on the work of glaciers

Glaciers — classification

Glaciers vary in size and location. The smallest are niche and cirque glaciers which occupy small hollows or valleys in upland areas. Valley glaciers are larger, moving down a pre-existing valley and supplied by a cirque or icefield. If a number of these reach lowland and subsequently merge, they are piedmont glaciers. Finally, ice caps and ice sheets completely cover large areas of continents.

You need to:

- be able to define the main types of glacier

Landforms of valley glaciation

The classic landforms of valley glaciation are distinctive.

	Characteristics
Cirque	• Armchair-shaped hollow with a steep back wall and rock basin • Frequently contains a lake behind a rock or moraine lip • Formed by nivation, plucking and rotational slip • In the UK, cirques have a broadly northerly orientation
Arête	• Formed by two cirques eroding back or sideways towards each other, leaving a steep-sided ridge
Pyramidal peak	• Formed by three or more cirques eroding into a mountain
Glacial trough	• A U-shaped valley formed by the passage of ice • The pre-existing valley is straightened and deepened by the glacier eroding it into the typical U-shape
Ribbon lake	• Lake formed in over-deep section of glacial trough
Rock step	• More resistant rock in floor of glacial trough
Truncated spur	• The steepened valley side formed by the removal of the tips of pre-existing interlocking spurs
Hanging valley	• Formed by differential erosion between the tributary valley and the main valley • The smaller one erodes less deeply, causing a large drop in valley floor level when the ice has melted, which produces a waterfall
Striations	• Scratches in rocks parallel to ice movement which are caused by the scraping of embedded rocks in the ice
Roche moutonnée	• A resistant rock with an abraded up-valley (stoss) slope and plucked down-valley slope
Crag and tail	• A large mass of resistant rock with a gently sloping tail of material in the lee protected by the crag

You need to:

- know the main landforms of valley glaciation
- be familiar with the characteristics of these landforms
- understand the formation of the landforms
- be able to give examples of such a landscape, including those in the UK and northwest Europe

Landforms of ice-sheet glaciation

As mentioned above, these landforms are the product of glacial and fluvioglacial processes.

Glacial landforms

	Characteristics
Till	Unsorted moraine deposited within the ice margin, often in large sheets of material, with the characteristics of the rocks eroded by the glacier
Moraine	• Material deposited when the ice has melted • It can be: — lateral (frost-shattered material carried on the sides of the glacier and deposited as an embankment on the valley side) — medial (the result of two lateral moraines merging and thus found in the middle of a valley) — terminal (a high linear mound of material deposited at the snout of a glacier, marking the maximum ice advance) — recessional (locations where the ice snout stopped long enough when retreating to build a moraine) — push (formed by an ice re-advance pushing previously deposited material into a mound)
Erratic	• A boulder transported by a glacier and deposited in an area of different geology
Drumlin	• A smooth elongated mound of till • The long axis is parallel to the flow, with the steep (stoss) end facing the flow and the gentler slope in the lee • Drumlins usually occur in swarms • Probably deposited beneath the ice when the glacier was unable to continue to transport its load

Meltwater plays a major part in the development of landforms in glacial areas, as it is present both within and outside the ice margin. Water flows at higher pressures within the ice, so can erode and transport more than a normal river. This provides more material for deposition outside the ice margin, particularly as these rivers will have a lower competence and capacity.

Fluvioglacial landforms

	Characteristics
Outwash plain	• Gravels, sands and clays deposited by meltwater flowing from the ice snout • Forms a gently sloping plain with braided streams flowing over it (see below) • Can be up to 75 m thick and also deposited on till as the ice retreats
Varve	• Layer of silt deposited annually in lakes near the ice margin • Coarser sand is deposited in spring and finer material in autumn as the flow of meltwater decreases
Kame	• Mound of sand and gravel deposited by streams at the ice front • One side collapses as the glacier melts • Can also be the result of englacial sediments being deposited as the glacier melts

	Characteristics
Kame terrace	• Sands and gravels deposited by a stream flowing along the side of the glacier, where melting is greater • Can be recognised by the collapsed side when the glacier melts
Esker	• Long sinuous ridge of sands and gravels • The result of sediment deposited by a meltwater stream flowing under the glacier • Formed as the glacier retreats
Kettle hole	• Depression formed when blocks of ice are covered by till or fluvioglacial deposits as the glacier melts • When the ice melts, the depression is formed
Braided stream	• Found on outwash plains in particular • The rivers are unable to transport the load because of reduced competence • This is a result of the seasonal variation in the amount of discharge between spring and autumn and the reduced flow in comparison with the pressure of flow in sub-glacial streams
Overflow channel	• This is formed by large amounts of meltwater becoming trapped between the glacier and high land • Eventually, the lowest point in the surrounding land is breached and a steep-sided overflow channel is cut by the escaping water

You need to:
- know the main landforms of ice sheet glaciation, both glacial and fluvioglacial
- be familiar with the characteristics of these landforms, both glacial and fluvioglacial
- understand the formation of the landforms, both glacial and fluvioglacial
- be able to give examples of such landscapes, including those in the UK and northwest Europe

Landscape processes — periglaciation

Periglacial processes are typically found at work near to the margin of an ice sheet, but the term is also used for areas of cold climate, such as alpine areas.

Permafrost is a characteristic feature of periglaciation. This is where the ground is permanently frozen for two consecutive summers. Continuous permafrost is found in the Arctic Circle, where mean temperatures are below –5°C. Permafrost is thought to reach depths of 700 m in Canada and 1500 m in Siberia.

Discontinuous permafrost lies further away from the poles, in areas with annual mean temperatures of –5°C to –1°C. It consists of islands of permanently frozen ground, separated by areas near to water bodies such as rivers, lakes and the sea.

Sporadic permafrost is found in areas with mean temperatures just below freezing point and summer temperatures well above freezing. This results in isolated areas of frozen ground.

The melting of the surface layers of soil in summer causes saturation. The water cannot percolate downwards because of the permafrost, so wetlands form. This surface layer is the active layer.

You need to:

- know the location of permafrost areas
- be able to give the definition of permafrost
- explore the variations in permafrost and their relative location
- understand the reasons for the formation of the active layer

Periglacial processes and landforms

The processes (already outlined) operating in periglacial environments are frost heave, frost shattering, nivation and solifluction. Ground contraction and freezing of ground-water form distinctive landforms, with the erosive action of running water and wind also occurring.

Periglacial landforms

	Characteristics
Stone polygon	• The growth of ice crystals beneath stones lifts them (heave) and when the ice thaws, finer material falls beneath and prevents them falling back to the original position • When they reach the surface, the repeated heaving moves the larger stones outwards to form small domed stone polygons, 1–5 m in diameter, in areas of low gradient • On slopes over 6°, the stones move downhill to form stone stripes
Ice wedge	• Ground contraction occurs in winter as freezing takes place and cracks appear • Meltwater, and particles that prevent the cracks closing, fill them the following summer • When freezing occurs the next winter, the cracks deepen and widen to form ice wedges • The polygons formed by this process have the stones in the middle in a depression
Pingos	• These are dome-shaped, isolated hills found only in sand • Open-system pingos are formed in valley floors in areas of thin or discontinuous permafrost by the re-freezing of surface water • This causes any overlying sediments to be pushed up into a mound as the ice expands • Closed-system pingos occur in low-lying areas of continuous permafrost • They frequently form on small lakes where the water is frozen both from above and from below by the permafrost • This freezing causes expansion and a dome is formed • It results in the downward growth of the permafrost • Both sorts of pingo can cause the surface to rupture, and if the ice core melts, collapse may occur, leaving a water-filled hollow

	Characteristics
Blockfields, scree, tors	• Freeze–thaw causes blocks of rock to be weathered from the parent material • Where these are on low gradient, they are known as blockfields • If the material falls to the base of a slope, it is known as scree or talus • The action of frost, with subsequent solifluction, is thought to form tors
Nivation hollow	• Small hollows are formed on hillsides by a combination of freeze–thaw, chemical weathering and solifluction
Solifluction	• The active layer flows slowly downslope to form solifluction lobes and sheets • The deposits are known as head in southern England • The process may also have formed the dry valleys in the chalk of southern England
Braided stream	• The result of seasonal variations in meltwater discharge and large amounts of river load
Loess	• Strong winds are able to pick up particles from periglacial areas, as there is little vegetation cover • This is redeposited as loess, a fertile soil • Loess covers much of northern Europe

You need to:
- understand the processes at work in periglacial areas
- know the landforms that result from these processes
- be able to give examples from the UK and northwest Europe, and from the Canadian Northlands

Synoptic links
- Unit 1, element 1
- Unit 4, element 2

Biomes and ecosystems

The tundra biome

The tundra biome extends, as mentioned above, across the extreme northern parts of Alaska, Canada, Russia and Scandinavia. It covers one-tenth of the world's land area. The landscape is barren, treeless and turns to a marshy plain in many areas in the summer.

It is a biome of very low productivity, with a net primary productivity of 140, which is second lowest only to the hot deserts. Insolation is low, the sun is low in the sky and there are many months of permanent night. Temperatures are below 6 °C, the standard minimum temperature for plant growth for most of the year. At best, there is a growing season of about 2 months. Thus plants have to complete their life cycles in 50–60 days. Water is unavailable for most of the year because it is frozen, except during the short summers, when soils frequently become waterlogged. Precipitation is low, and the climate is defined as cold desert.

The vegetation is tolerant of low temperatures and moisture deficiency. There are fewer species of plants than in any other biome and these are slow growing. Plants grow close to the ground because of the strong winds and they also suffer the effects of increased evapotranspiration in stronger winds.

The lack of nitrogen-fixing plants limits fertility, and the cold and wet conditions reduce the rates of decomposition. The lack of sunlight and water hinders photosynthesis, but there is a longer food chain than might be expected. The mosses and lichens have a high sugar content, which supports herbivores such as reindeer and musk ox. The herbivores must migrate to obtain sufficient food that is not snow-covered. Carnivores include wolves and arctic foxes.

There are five types of dominant plant, each occupying its own specialised niche: lichens, mosses, grasses, cushion plants and low shrubs. The environments in which these are typically found are shown below.

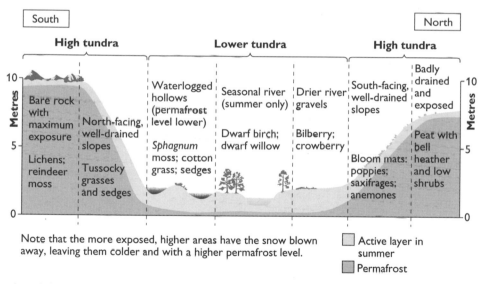

Note that the more exposed, higher areas have the snow blown away, leaving them colder and with a higher permafrost level.

□ Active layer in summer
■ Permafrost

The alpine tundra has similar vegetation types, again set in their own niches. The productivity is again low because of the low temperatures, but insolation may well be higher. The growth of plants is thus restricted by the cold. Precipitation is variable (depending on the altitude), but will be snow in winter.

You need to:
- know the distribution of the tundra biome
- explore the variations in the nature of the tundra biome
- understand ecological productivity and the controls on this
- be able to explain the alpine tundra variant

Tundra soils

These are uniform in one respect: they lack clearly differentiated horizons. The limited vegetation restricts litter, there are few soil organisms, and slow rates of decomposition therefore cause a thin layer of peat, either very acidic humus or mor, to form. Limited percolation occurs in spring, releasing iron. The permafrost prevents drainage and causes waterlogging in summer, allowing gleying to take place. When freezing occurs in the autumn, the horizons become further distorted and churned. Where bedrock is close to the surface, frost heave raises fragments to the surface to form stone polygons and stone stripes. A typical soil profile is set out below.

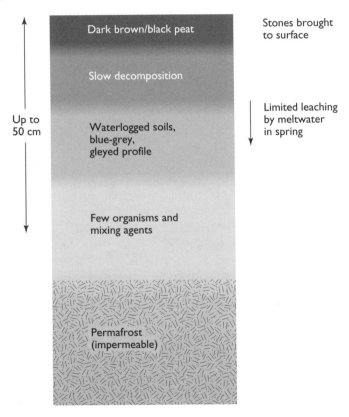

In alpine areas, the soils tend to be very thin and stony — typical of mountain soils. They are azonal, i.e. are permanently immature, as the soil has little time to develop because of the climatic influences and the steepness of slope.

You need to:
- understand the conditions in which tundra soils form
- explore the processes at work in tundra soils
- understand the characteristics of a typical soil profile
- know the alpine variant

The tundra — a unique and fragile biome

The tundra is a unique biome, as demonstrated by the climatic controls and the limited productivity. It is also very fragile, for a number of reasons.

The slow rate of plant growth means that any disruption to the ecosystem takes a long time to be restored — at least 50 years. For example, tyre tracks will take this length of time to be re-vegetated. The low productivity and limited species diversity means that the plants are very specialised and any disruption causes difficulty in regeneration; species are unable to adapt to new environments. Soils are not fully developed and disruption will mean that plants are unable to re-grow easily.

Food chains are liable to wild fluctuations in the energy held in each trophic level as populations change rapidly in number. For example, the number of arctic owls is strongly related to the number of lemmings, or the number of arctic foxes to the number of arctic hares. Both of these herbivore populations are liable to long and short-term fluctuations, with consequent fluctuations in the populations of carnivores.

Any disruption to the functioning of the ecosystem or biome has long-term implications; hence the fragility of the environment. There is great concern over any exploitation of resources in tundra areas. These points apply equally to alpine areas.

You need to:
- be aware of the uniqueness of the tundra biome and the reasons for this
- understand the concept of fragility as applied to the tundra biome

The Southern Ocean ecosystems

The Southern Ocean, the ocean surrounding Antarctica, is one of the most productive marine ecosystems. In the westerly wind belt, the waters provide ideal conditions for the growth of krill, which is the basis of the higher levels of the marine food chain. Krill feed on phytoplankton.

The rate of growth of the krill means that the productivity of the Southern Ocean is very great and this causes the energy pyramid to become inverted, in that the lowest trophic level is smaller than those above, but reproduces very quickly. The upper levels, above the krill, follow the typical pattern of energy change. Krill support the carnivores of the Southern Ocean, i.e. fish, penguins, whales, seals and sea birds.

You need to:
- know the location of the Southern Ocean
- be aware of the productivity levels of the Southern Ocean
- understand the trophic pyramid of the Southern Ocean

Synoptic links
- Unit 1, element 3

Human activity, economic processes and resource management

Economic activity

The traditional economic activity in tundra areas was that of hunting, agriculture being impossible. The Inuit, for example, lived entirely off the resources provided by fishing and the trapping of seals and smaller mammals. Caribou and whales also provided a food supply. The Lapps based their economic activity on the herding of reindeer. These people migrated with their food supplies and according to the seasons. This type of activity was fully sustainable, but would only support a low density of population.

The next wave of activity came in North America and Russia in the seventeenth to nineteenth centuries, when newcomers came to these areas for sealing, whaling, fur trapping and mining. Mining led to the establishment of permanent settlements, but the other activities tended to be more temporary, or seasonal.

More recent exploitation has been on a larger scale and has had a dramatic impact on the lifestyle of the indigenous population. Activities include mining, hydroelectric power (HEP), fishing and tourism. Alaska's north shore has been settled for the exploitation of oil. Military, strategic and geo-political concerns have given these areas increasing importance, particularly in Alaska and northern Russia.

Farming, with the development of fast-growing crops, has been possible in certain areas, such as the Mackenzie River basin in Canada. The Canadian Northlands of Siberia and Alaska have been settled for these activities to take place. These are essentially new areas for tourism, and the demand is increasing each year.

In alpine regions, the main economic activity is tourism. This takes advantage of the winter conditions for skiing and other snow-based sports. Mountain climbing is also a feature of such regions. In summer, tourism in the beautiful glaciated upland scenery is important. HEP makes a significant contribution to power supply in these regions.

You need to:
- study the traditional economic activities of people in cold climates
- be familiar with the recent changes to economic activity
- know the nature of economic activity in alpine regions

The physical–human impacts

The physical environment has a great impact on human activity and, in a two-way relationship, people also have an impact on the physical environment. This relationship is summarised in the tables below.

Physical–human

Factor	Effect
Low temperature	Low temperatures (below freezing for most of the year) limit human activity
Low insolation	Short summers and growing season
Low precipitation	Low total, hence desert, but is frozen for most of year, so is unavailable
Limited vegetation	Low-growing, few species
Poor soils	Temperatures too low for biota and chemical reactions to work to break down the limited organic material; therefore thin, stony, poorly developed
Snowy, steep slopes	Limited sites for settlement
Blizzards	Strong winds and snow drifting cause windchill and whiteout conditions

Human–physical

Factor	Effect
Minerals	Settlement and construction of infrastructure, including pipelines for oil, airstrips etc. — cause damage to the environment
Hunting	Seal hunting and fishing — likely to lead to over-exploitation
Tourism	Destruction of environment by removal of vegetation, increase in avalanches; litter/waste does not degrade
Transport	Risk of oil pollution from spillages; road vehicles churn up the ground
Air pollution	Global warming is causing change to environments as temperatures rise; permafrost melts as does snow and glaciers, with effects on ski tourism becoming apparent
Thermokarst	Human activity causes permafrost to melt by the removal of vegetation, centrally heated buildings, oil, water and sewerage pipes, drilling for oil and gas, and road construction; this can be avoided by building airstrips and roads on gravel pads, and putting buildings, oil tanks and pipelines on stilts etc.

You need to:
- be aware of the impact of the physical environment on people
- understand the effects of people on the environment
- be able to give two case studies from the Canadian Northlands, Alaska, Antarctica and the Alps

Synoptic links
- Unit 1, element 3
- Unit 5, elements 1 and 3

Present problems and future issues

Settlement, transport and local cultures

The increasing settlement and development of transport links has resulted in a great impact on the local, indigenous peoples. The influx of a relatively large number of people and the infrastructure they bring with them, including a cash economy, has caused the traditional nomadic way of life to change. For example, many Inuit are now more sedentary and living in towns, and they tend to be dependent on benefits and often not well adapted to an urban way of life. Improvements in transport have allowed more outsiders to come in and resources to be taken out.

You need to:
- be aware of the impact that recent settlement, transport improvements and in-migration have had on the indigenous population and on their way of life

Conservation and sustainability

The conservation of wilderness areas has become increasingly important in recent years. There is a very strong sentiment in favour of conservation, but this is equally opposed by businesses which are keen to exploit natural resources. For example, much of Alaska has been designated a National Park because of its wilderness. In 2001, President Bush passed legislation that would allow oil companies to drill for oil in a protected area on the north shore. The justification was that the national interest in terms of energy supply outweighed the need for conservation. Such issues will become more common as oil and other resources become more scarce.

As the environment in areas of cold climates is fragile, any development has the potential to cause serious damage. Sustainable development is therefore far more difficult to achieve in such regions. Antarctica has been spared any development by international agreement for over 40 years, as it is such a fragile environment. This still holds, but is coming under pressure. Tourism is the main recent development, but has to be by cruise ship, as hotels and other facilities are prohibited on the continent. The Southern Ocean surrounding Antarctica is being exploited for fish, particularly around the Falklands. In addition, oil and gas exploration is taking place.

Similar issues arise in the Alps, where deforestation for the creation of ski-runs has destabilised slopes and increased the risk of avalanches and rockslides. There is severe environmental degradation taking place in these areas after many years of the development of the tourist industry.

Other areas, such as the Canadian Northlands and the Lake District or Snowdonia in the UK, are experiencing similar challenges. It is essential to study the unique landscape and characteristics of at least one of these areas, along with the development of, and changes to, the tourist industry and other economic activities, in order to bring out the relevant issues.

A study of these cold-climate areas brings into sharp relief the different interest groups involved, and their potential for disagreement over the use of the environment. You must be aware of these groups and their viewpoints in order to analyse the values of decision-makers. You must also consider your own values and attitudes about these issues.

You need to:

- understand the reasons for conservation in wilderness areas
- be familiar with the issues surrounding sustainability in fragile environments such as regions of cold climates
- be able to describe case studies of the issues surrounding sustainability from Alaska, the Alps, the Canadian Northlands, Antarctica and the Southern Ocean
- be able to give an example of a case study of change from the Lake District or Snowdonia
- analyse the values and attitudes of decision-makers (and your own) about sustainability in these areas

> **Synoptic links**
> - Unit 1, elements 1 and 3
> - Unit 2, elements 1, 2 and 3
> - Unit 5, elements 1 and 3

Questions & Answers

This concluding section of the guide contains three typical resource-based questions (Section A) and three essay questions (Section B), based on the topic areas outlined in the Content Guidance section.

Please note that in the examination you will have to answer two resource-based questions and one essay from those set.

Model answers are given after the questions. These are provided at a typical grade-C standard (Candidate A) and a good grade-A standard (Candidate B).

Examiner's comments

These are preceded by the icon ℮. They are interspersed in the answers and indicate where credit is due. In the weaker answers, they also point out areas for improvement, specific problems and common errors such as poor time management, lack of clarity, weak or non-existent development, irrelevance, misinterpretation of the question and mistaken meanings of terms.

In Section A, parts (a) and (b), marks are awarded by points. In Section A part (c) and Section B, marks are awarded by Level (see pages 8–9).

Section A (part (c))	Section B
Level 1: 1–3 marks	Level 1: 1–6 marks
Level 2: 4–5 marks	Level 2: 7–12 marks
Level 3: 6–7 marks	Level 3: 13–18 marks
	Level 4: 19–24 marks
	Level 5: 25–30 marks

Section A

Coast processes and problems

Question 1

(a) **What are the causes of sea-level change?** (4 marks)

(b) **Outline the characteristics of two landforms formed by a change in sea level.** (4 marks)

(c) **Explain the advantages for people that may occur as a result of changes in sea level.** (7 marks)

■ ■ ■

Answer to question 1: Candidate A

(a) Sea-level changes are the result of isostatic and eustatic changes. Isostatic changes are the result of a change of land level, whereas eustatic are changes caused by a change in sea level.

> *e* Candidate A has correctly identified the causes of sea-level changes, but at a broad level of understanding, with some important detail lacking. This answer is awarded 2 marks.

(b) A raised beach consists of material deposited at an old sea level above the current one. The material is rounded and found at the back of the old beach. It may well be shingle cemented together. A ria is a drowned river valley in an area of upland. It forms excellent harbours.

> *e* Two valid landforms have been identified. The raised beach is described well, with mention of the location of the material on the old shoreline and the type of material. The ria is described more generally and there is an unnecessary mention of its uses. This response gains 3 out of 4 marks.

(c) Changes in sea level offer many opportunities to people. A rise in sea level floods valleys, giving rise to rias and fjords. These make excellent harbours, such as Falmouth (a ria) and Hardanger Fjord, in Norway. Another benefit is that these two features can be used for transport inland, particularly where the valley sides are very steep. Natural deltas form at the heads of the arms of the valleys and these are used for potential sites for settlement. Raised beaches and the associated relict shorelines also allow settlement to be located above the sea and thus avoid flooding, as in western Scotland.

> *e* This answer identifies valid benefits. Examples are present, but are not used consistently. This is a Level 2 response worth 4 marks.

■ ■ ■

Answer to question 1: Candidate B

(a) Sea-level changes, otherwise known as base-level changes, occur for two reasons. Isostatic changes are when the Earth's crust is depressed by the weight of ice or sediment (a rise in base level) or the crust rises after the weight is removed (a fall in base level). Eustatic changes are the result of global changes as a consequence of the melting of the ice caps (rise in base level) or the formation of ice caps (fall in base level).

> *e* This is a complete answer, with clear definitions of both causes, for 4 marks. The knowledge of base level demonstrates full understanding of the topic.

(b) The two landforms are a fjord and a ria. A fjord is a drowned upland glaciated valley. The west coast of Norway has a number of these, Hardanger Fjord being a good example. They have steep sides, the typical U-shape, and are elongated, being relatively straight. There is a threshold at the mouth, where shallower water is found. At the heads of the arms of the fjord, deltas are found where inflowing rivers deposit sediment.

The ria is a drowned upland river valley. Southwest England has a number of examples, including Carrick Roads, Falmouth. The sides are relatively gentle, with small cliffs near the seaward end. The underwater profile increases in depth towards the sea. In plan, they show a typical river pattern with interlocking spurs.

> *e* This response is a detailed description of two appropriate landforms; the command word is followed carefully. There are examples in support of both cases. This gains the full 4 marks.

(c) Sea-level changes have many benefits for people. Settlement sites are provided by raised shorelines, as on the west coast of Scotland, as the flat land just above the sea is very suitable. Similarly in Norway, the deltas at the heads of fjords are the only areas of flat land for settlement in a mountainous area.

The sheltered deepwater harbours provided by both fjords and rias have been of great economic advantage, particularly for Norway (Trondheim Fjord), providing access inland and to the sea. The fjords also allow warmer water and air to pass inland to relieve the winter climate. The spectacular fjord coastline has encouraged the growth of tourism too, with cruises along the fjord coast to the North Cape being popular. Fishing and a marine tradition have been encouraged as well by the access provided by the fjords. These points about fjords would also apply to the rias in Cornwall in the UK, such as Plymouth Sound.

> *e* Candidate B covers a variety of landforms. Those used clearly show the benefits, with valid support, particularly when referring to Norway. There is detailed understanding, several points with examples, and an effective style. The answer uses specialist vocabulary, which is focused on the requirements of the question. This is clearly a good Level 3 response and is awarded the full 7 marks.

Geomorphological processes and hazards

Question 2

(a) Distinguish between weathering and mass movement.   (4 marks)
(b) Outline the factors that influence mass movement.   (4 marks)
(c) Explain the ways in which mass movement can be seen as a hazard.   (7 marks)

■ ■ ■

Answer to question 2: Candidate A

(a) Weathering is the break-up of rocks in situ by the agents of weather at the surface. Mass movement is the downslope movement of weathered material under the influence of gravity.

🖉 These two definitions are correct, but the candidate fails to distinguish between the two. Using a term such as 'whereas' or 'on the other hand' would have been sufficient to contrast the two. This response is credited with 3 marks out of 4.

(b) Mass movement is controlled by a number of factors, the main ones being gravity and the amount of water available. The influence of gravity affects the speed of movement, especially when the amount of water is also high. This causes the fast movements such as flows and falls to be more effective. Creep occurs on slopes of low angle, and does not always involve water. Falls involve gravity, but not water, except for avalanches.

🖉 The candidate names the correct factors, but the outline demonstrates some confusion in approach, and the points are muddled in expression. This gains only 3 out of the 4 marks available, as the factors are not linked clearly to the movements.

(c) Mass movement is a hazard when it affects people. The slow movements, such as creep, are not hazardous, but the fast movements are. For example, avalanches kill people yearly in the Alps, particularly in the skiing resorts. Landslides are a hazard as large amounts of debris are involved in a rapid movement, particularly in coastal areas. Mudflows are possibly the most rapid movements; when Nevado del Ruiz erupted, the melting ice at the top of the mountain caused a mudflow that moved so quickly that 20 000 people were killed. Rockfalls can be hazardous in mountainous areas.

🖉 The candidate has a partial knowledge of a hazard, omitting damage to property from the definition. The statement that slow movements are not a hazard is also suspect. However, the other points are valid and support is present, if variable in depth, ranging from the detailed to the generalised. The explanation is therefore partial, making this a Level 2 response, worth 5 marks.

Answer to question 2: Candidate B

(a) Weathering is the disintegration of rocks in situ by the agents of weather at the surface of the Earth. On the other hand, mass movement is the downslope movement of weathered material (regolith) under the influence of gravity.

ℓ This response is accurate, with a clear distinction made for full marks.

(b) Mass movement is controlled by gravity and the related angle of slope. The steeper the slope, the faster is the movement. In addition, the availability of water affects the type and speed of movement. Water will increase the weight of a rock and thus trigger movement in a rotational slide, where the slip planes are lubricated. Water comprises a great proportion of flows, including earthflows, solifluction and mudflows. On the other hand, gravity is the main factor at work in falls and avalanches. Creep involves gravity for the most part.

ℓ This response covers the main factors in some detail and is able to apply the factors to the types of movement. All scales of movement are mentioned and therefore the response gains the full 4 marks.

(c) Mass movement can be a hazard at all scales of movement. A hazard affects people and/or property. Creep can cause walls to collapse and roads to tear, as happened at Crockenhill, Kent. Solifluction, a slow flow process in periglacial areas, causes instability on slopes. Earthflows and mudflows are faster and provide more of a hazard. Earthflows have threatened housing in some South Wales valleys, while the mudflow following the volcanic eruption of Nevado del Ruiz and arising from the melting of the glacier killed over 20 000 people. Landslides are frequent in coastal areas; the collapse of Holbeck Hall Hotel is a well-known example. Avalanches and rockfalls are frequent in mountainous areas; the former kill many people each year in skiing areas of the Alps. Therefore, all types of mass movement, from slow to fast, can cause hazards to people.

ℓ This is a very full response. The candidate covers all types of movement and supports the great majority with examples, the detail of which varies a little. This is a clear Level 3 response, gaining full marks.

Cold environments and human activity

Question 3

(a) What are the differences between warm and cold glaciers? (4 marks)
(b) Outline the processes of glacial erosion. (4 marks)
(c) Explain the landforms associated with valley glaciation. (7 marks)

■ ■ ■

Answer to question 3: Candidate A

(a) Warm glaciers have ice about freezing point, whereas cold ones have a lower temperature. This affects the way the ice flows, the rate of erosion and the amount transported.

e This is an adequate response. The candidate is able to identify, in a straightforward manner, the main differences between the glaciers, but without the detail to put these differences into context. This gains 2 out of the 4 marks available.

(b) Glaciers erode in a number of ways. The main processes are plucking, abrasion and rotational slip. Plucking is when the ice freezes to the rock, and as the glacier moves, it pulls the rock fragment away. Abrasion is when the debris transported in the ice scratches the sides and base of the glacial valley. Rotational slip is when the ice rotates and overdeepens a hollow, as in the erosion of a cirque.

e This is a reasonable answer, covering three of the processes of erosion and describing the ways in which they operate. There are others that could have been covered. The terminology is appropriate, but the outline is very brief, so this gains 3 marks out of 4.

(c) The landforms of valley glaciation are distinctive. At the head, cirques, arêtes and pyramidal peaks are found. These are formed by erosion, i.e. rotational slip, scouring out an armchair-shaped hollow (the cirque). The erosion of the cirque backwall and sides forms the arête (a steep-sided ridge between two cirques) and the pyramidal peak (three or more cirques eroding a steep-sided peak). The ice moves down to the main glacier, which forms a deep, steep-sided valley that straightens off the pre-existing one. At the end of the glacier are moraines. There may be lakes formed when the ice has melted, both on the cirque and in the main valley (ribbon lakes).

e This response starts off well. The detail on the cirque, arête and pyramidal peak is explanatory. The depth does fade a little as the candidate moves down valley, and the depositional landforms are not fully developed or explained. There is no specific support, so the response is at Level 2 and is awarded 5 marks.

section

Answer to question 3: Candidate B

(a) The two types of glacier have different characteristics. Warm glaciers maintain a temperature close to freezing point throughout, and are therefore continually melting and re-freezing. This enables them to erode, transport and deposit both by ice and by meltwater, which is freely available. Velocity is also greater. In contrast, cold glaciers have a temperature permanently below freezing throughout, so they lack meltwater. They are unable to erode, transport and deposit to the same extent as warm glaciers, and have a lower velocity.

e This is a very full response, which is worth 4 marks.

(b) The action of weathering and the provision of meltwater in weakening the rocks make all processes of glacial erosion more effective. Plucking removes shattered rocks by ice re-freezing to them and removing the fragments as the glacier moves on. Abrasion uses the fragments to scour the sides and base, removing weathered material and scraping away the solid rock. Rotational slip helps the over-deepening of cirques by increasing the pressure to remove fragments at the base of the cirque. Extending and compressing flow increases and decreases the velocity and thus the rate of erosion as the ice moves down valley.

e This response covers all of the main processes of erosion and gives additional comment to observe the command word. This is worth the full 4 marks.

(c) The landforms of valley glaciation are the products of both erosion and deposition. At the head, most are erosional, with cirques, arêtes and pyramidal peaks the main landforms. Cirques are formed as rotation deepens the hollow, while erosion of the head and sides causes the narrow-ridged arête (two cirque walls back-to-back) and the pyramidal peak (three cirque walls). Frequently, there is a lake (tarn) in the cirque formed either by a rock lip or a moraine dam. Hanging valleys form where the tributary valley meets the main valley. The difference in the weight of ice causes the main valley to become deeper; after melting, the tributary valley hangs above the main one, often with a waterfall. The differential erosion of the valley causes rock steps (where the rock is more resistant) and rock basins. These fill to form ribbon lakes, again with a rock or moraine lip. The ice in the main valley cuts off the previous valley spurs to form truncated spurs. As the glacier moves from the valley, it deposits the moraine, carried after weathering from the sides and base. This deposition can be at the snout (terminal), sides (lateral) and base (ground). Other material transported on the ice becomes kames or kame terraces. Depositional landforms can be found anywhere, as they were deposited as the ice retreated.

e This response covers the variety of landforms that are associated with valley glaciation. Their formation is explained and the links between the different types of landform are clear. This is a detailed response and gains the full 7 marks.

Section B

Essays

Question 4

The management of coastal areas is for one purpose, but has many outcomes.
Discuss this statement. (30 marks)

Question 5

Geomorphological hazards have similar effects. To what extent do responses
vary in different parts of the world? (30 marks)

Question 6

Glaciated areas provide many opportunities for sustainable economic
development. Discuss this statement. (30 marks)

You must bear in mind that questions 4, 5 and 6 are synoptic in nature. In your response to
these questions, you are required to show your knowledge and understanding of different
aspects of geography, the connections between these different aspects and, where relevant,
human perspectives upon geographical themes and issues. The synoptic elements are considered by the inclusion of at least one of these three themes: physical–human relationships,
sustainability or environmental.

■ ■ ■

Answer to question 4: Candidate A

If the management of coastal areas has one purpose, it is to protect the coastline and
property behind it. The outcomes are more varied, because the results are not always
those expected. This essay will explore both of these points and will attempt to come
to a reasoned conclusion.

The management of coasts is a complicated issue. The coastline is a very complex
system. There are variations in the inputs, the stores, the transfers and, finally, the
outputs. Coastal management is usually to defend the coast from erosion. This has
been the case for many years and great sums of money have been spent in such
undertakings. For example, at Hastings, in East Sussex, coastal management has been
undertaken since the nineteenth century. The area of coast around Hastings has been
subject to erosion for hundreds of years, as can be seen from the fact that the castle,
built in the twelfth century, is now half eroded as the cliff line has retreated since
then.

The growth of Hastings as an urban centre occurred in the nineteenth century,
after the arrival of the railway, and coastal management has increased ever since.
This has culminated in major investment in the last 25 years in coastal defences
around the town. The sea front has a large sea wall and the beach has been built up
to protect the town. Groynes have been established at regular intervals and the beach
has been replenished by nourishment from offshore dredging.

The need for nourishment was the result of longshore drift, which was causing the beach to be removed and the sea defences to be undermined. It was the building of the harbour wall and its refurbishment that allowed the beach to be built up greatly to the east of the town. It is now approximately 100 m wide by the harbour wall, as longshore drift has moved shingle to accumulate against it. To the east of the harbour wall, within the harbour, the beach is much thinner in the harbour itself, and further along the coast, to the east of the harbour, where there are no break-waters, the cliffs of East Hill are exposed to direct erosion as there is virtually no beach material.

This clearly shows the importance of the management of the coast to the well-being of Hastings. However, there have been some unexpected downcoast effects. The coastal areas downdrift, i.e. in the direction of longshore drift, have been exposed to greater erosion as the supply of beach material has been cut off by the groynes, breakwaters and the harbour wall at Hastings. This has resulted in more expenditure at Fairlight village, where an offshore reef has been constructed to reduce wave energy. At Cliff End, beach nourishment and the construction of revetments have been necessary to protect the settlement and Romney Marsh behind the sea wall.

Therefore, it can be seen that coastal management at Hastings has been successful, but has had the effect of causing further problems down the coast.

> *e* This response is competent. There is a clear essay format, with an introduction and conclusion. There is good use of exemplar material in a constructive manner, to meet the demands of the question. However, Candidate A does not go beyond agreement, by implication, with the first statement, and although there is reference to more than one outcome, the development is more limited. There are a number of reasons for the schemes of management, for example, which are not discussed. Although there is some evidence of synopticity, this is linked to the process and is not a well-developed theme of the essay. This essay reaches the second Level (19–24 marks), as there is some synopticity, but would be towards the lower end.

■ ■ ■

Answer to question 4: Candidate B

The statement that coastal management is for one purpose is open to some debate, but there are usually a number of outcomes, some of which are expected and others unexpected.

In the case of Hastings in East Sussex, coastal management has been implemented for a number of reasons. These include the erosion of the beach by longshore drift, the need to prevent coastal erosion of the built up area of the town, the need to maintain the attractiveness of the town for tourists and the need to provide a harbour for the long-established fishing fleet.

The schemes of coastal management at Hastings started in the nineteenth century, but after the building of the harbour wall in the 1920s, the main period of activity was in the last quarter of the twentieth century. A major scheme was set in motion, costing over £4.5 million. This involved the renewal of the groynes and breakwaters close to the centre of the town, and then a programme of beach nourishment to raise the level of the beach shingle and protect the newly replaced sea walls. Before this programme, the beach was wide updrift of the harbour wall, but was very narrow at high tide by the pier.

This programme was successful in terms of the town itself. The beach is now higher and wider and thus protects the coastline where the coastal defences are in place. The new shingle beach is attractive to tourists, but the sand exposed at low tide still has little to commend it. The harbour is still open for the fishing fleet, being protected by the harbour wall and a breakwater.

However, the downdrift effects had unexpected consequences. The direction of longshore drift is eastwards up the Channel. Thus, areas to the east of the town beyond the breakwaters have had no beach to protect the cliffs. Erosion has increased as the work at Hastings has reduced the supply of beach material. This can be seen at a number of locations along the coast.

At Fairlight Glen, a major landslide/slump occurred as the cliffs, which contained much clay, collapsed suddenly. This did not affect people to a great extent. It was caused by classic overloading, as the weight of the cliff was increased by water saturating the clays and the clays were lubricated by the water. There was also under-mining at the base of the cliff by the sea.

At Fairlight, increased erosion threatens the village. In order to protect the village, an offshore reef has been constructed to reduce the power of the waves and to encourage the build up of a beach. Further along, at Cliff End, the existing sea wall is under threat as the beach is being eroded by longshore drift and the shingle is not being replaced from the direction of Hastings. Beach nourishment has been carried out, as has the upgrading of the revetments. If this sea wall is breached, not only is Cliff End under threat, but also Romney Marsh.

Therefore, the coastal management at Hastings has had a number of effects downdrift that were unexpected. However, to put this into context, other parts of the coastline in England have been managed in different ways. The strategy of managed retreat is one that allows certain coastal areas to be lost to the sea, rather than defend them. This can be seen as working with nature, rather than against it. The strategy tends to be used when the land is not settled, and so has less overall value. This is being applied in parts of East Anglia, though farmers and the National Farmers Union oppose it.

It is also worth mentioning that, although many areas are being defended, others are still being lost to the sea, despite the expenditure on coastal management. The cliffs at Shanklin Chine have collapsed recently, threatening a number of homes and hotels. It appears to be impossible to stabilise these cliffs because of their inherent unstable constituents of clays and weak sands.

In summary, the management of coastal areas has more than one purpose and several outcomes, not all of which are anticipated at the planning stages.

🖉 This is a very good response. Candidate B shows a clear essay style and responds to the requirements of the question. Several case studies are used effectively. Synopticity is demonstrated by the links with coastal processes and mass movement, both found in other elements of the specification. This essay is in the top Level (25–30 out of 30 marks), towards the upper end, if not at the very top.

■ ■ ■

Answer to question 5: Candidate A

Geomorpological hazards may indeed have similar effects, in that they cause harm to people and property, but the responses vary according to the part of the world in which the event occurs. Geomorphological hazards include earthquakes and volcanoes, both of which have a wide global distribution.

The effects of these hazards are similar in many ways. They all cause property to be damaged and human casualties. Volcanoes have a varying effect on people. This is because the type of eruption allows responses at different time scales. For example, very few people are killed by lava flows, as there is usually time to escape the hazard. Only the fastest basic lava flows are life-threatening, as most settlement is at some distance from the crater. On the other hand, gases in the form of nuées ardentes are fatal because of the speed at which they travel. A recent example of these was Mount St Helens, and from long ago, Pompeii, which was overcome by an eruption by Mount Vesuvius.

Lava flows do, however, cause a lot of damage, depending on the track. For example, the erupting volcano destroyed much of Heimaey, while the slopes of Mounts Etna and Vesuvius lose many olive and citrus groves during eruptions.

Earthquakes cause much damage to both property and people, depending on the intensity of the event. There are two effects to be recognised: primary and secondary. The former is caused by the event and includes damage to buildings, infrastructure and so on. Secondary damage is the result of the primary, and includes the threat of fire from broken gas pipes, water and food shortages and disease as the infrastructure is destroyed. These secondary effects are similar, regardless of the type of hazard.

The responses to the hazardous events do vary spatially. The most important factor is the level of economic development of the area, which affects the resources available and the cultural background of the victims. The amount of money available has a great impact in a number of ways. The preparations for the hazard vary. MEDCs like the USA can afford to spend on research to predict the events. They have emergency plans to respond after the event and can offer government help very quickly. People themselves may have insurance and can take measures to protect buildings, either during construction or later. This is illustrated when earthquakes occur in the USA, such as in Los Angeles in 1994 when 57 people were killed.

In LEDCs, resources are fewer, so people tend to have two responses: to avoid or flee the area, or to tolerate the events. The earthquake in central India, also in 1994, killed over 22 000 people. This was a result of the great number of unstrengthened buildings which collapsed, the fact that the earthquake came at night when people were asleep, and the subsequent loss of life from disease and shortages of food and water.

Thus, it can be demonstrated that geomorphological hazards do have similar effects, but that the responses do vary in different parts of the world.

> 🖉 Candidate B shows a clear and well developed essay structure here. The content is relevant, including definitions, but is restricted to just two hazards: earthquakes and volcanoes. The command words that require evaluation are covered in the conclusion, but not as a strong theme in the essay. Although the theme of the essay is dealt with, there is very little, if any, synoptic content. This essay would therefore be at the upper end of Level 3, gaining 13–18 out of the 30 marks available.

■ ■ ■

Answer to question 5: Candidate B

Geomorphological hazards include those caused by plate tectonics (earthquakes and volcanoes), and weathering and mass movement. A hazard is defined as an event that will cause damage to people and/or property. As a rule, the impact of such a hazard is broadly similar, but it is also true that the wealth of an area in terms of GNP per head will have an influence on the impact, as well as on the response.

To the extent that the effects of the hazards are similar, it is true that damage, destruction and casualties are consequences of a hazard event. How much this varies depends on the wealth of the area concerned. For example, the Los Angeles earthquake caused only 57 deaths in comparison with the 22 000 in a similar event in India later that year. The reasons for this are complex, but identifiable. With regard to prevention, the USA spends much on research to try to predict earthquakes. India does also have the facility for such research available, and frequently MEDCs have their own teams working with the local LEDC universities. It is impossible to predict earthquakes confidently anywhere in the world, so other factors must be important in explaining the different casualty figures.

The GNP per head of the two countries has a great impact on the response in terms of construction. The USA has strongly enforced building codes. These insist on steel frames for tall constructions so they can sway during an event. Buildings must have foundations embedded in solid rock. Road bridges now have rubber in the base of their columns to allow swaying. In India, very few of these codes can be established. Many were killed by the local materials in use that could not cope with the intensity of the earthquake, while communications broke down after the event.

In addition, the USA had emergency response plans. These were rehearsed, and education programmes were in operation for all. The fire, police and other emergency teams were well trained. In India, this was not the case. In the USA, the emergency teams went into action very quickly after the event, controlling fires and rescuing trapped people. The response in India was less effective, because the resources and training were not available. Emergency food, water and shelter was made available very quickly in the USA, but in India, much had to be sent in from MEDCs using NGOs.

Similar points can be made about other hazards. Volcanic eruptions tend not to be fatal in themselves, as the lava takes some time to reach populated areas. However, nuées ardentes (glowing clouds) travel very quickly and can cause many casualties. Recent examples include Mount St Helens, in which survivors talked about the heat of the clouds that passed near them. A total of 63 people died in this eruption, but it was in a remote area of the USA. Pompeii is a historical reminder of a town being overwhelmed. The island of Monserrat was evacuated when the volcano erupted, and the country struggled to cope with the disruption.

Mass movements tend to be destructive wherever they occur. However, the predictive element is stronger in MEDCs, so warning can be given. Even so, rapid movements can be destructive and equally dangerous in rich and poor countries. The mudflow resulting from the eruption of Nevado del Ruiz in Colombia killed 21 000 as it hit the town of Almero at 80 km h^{-1}. In comparison, the Aberfan disaster in the UK, when a coal tip flowed into a village in 1966, killed 147 people. Emergency help came quickly in the UK, whereas in Colombia the area was remote and time elapsed before the maximum response was in place. The effects of food and water shortages and disease were more important in the latter example.

In summary, geomorphological hazards can have similar effects, but the remoteness of the area will have a strong effect on casualties. Responses do vary in different parts of the world, reflecting the level of economic development in LEDCs and MEDCs, but responses also vary according to the remoteness of the area, the willingness of the people to be prepared and the response to the event which may be culturally influenced. A simple relationship based on wealth is not always valid.

> *e* This is a detailed response. The essay format is clear and well developed. The evaluation requirement is prominent and cases are detailed and consistent. The synoptic element is present with references to levels of economic development and to hazards from different elements of the unit. This is in the upper end of the top Level (25–30 out of 30 marks), and could even gain full marks.

Answer to question 6: Candidate A

Glaciated areas do provide opportunities for economic development, but sustainability may not always be possible. Sustainability is economic development to meet demand without long-term damage to the environment.

This essay will focus on the Alps, a well-known area which is currently glaciated, and which has a number of economic activities. The main activities are agriculture, forestry and tourism.

Traditionally, the highest alpine areas had no economic impact, being ice- and snow-covered all year. The areas of alpine vegetation, a variant of tundra vegetation, had some use for agriculture, mainly as poor grazing. The main activity was dairy herding on the grassy high summer slopes (alps) above the tree line, with a return to the lower valleys for winter. This environment is very fragile and only small amounts of grazing could be accommodated, especially on the tundra vegetation, which is snow-covered in winter, and where it takes up to 60 years for vegetation to re-grow after destruction.

The coniferous woodland areas are below the tree line, by definition, but are in the area that was glaciated in the recent past. The wood was used for fuel, especially in winter, and exported to other areas for use in construction and paper-making, for example. Many of the slopes have been deforested and this has caused significant problems for people, increasing the number of avalanches and also increasing slope instability over time. Thus, sustainability is compromised unless re-afforestation occurs.

Tourism has become one of the economic mainstays of these glaciated areas. It started in the late-nineteenth century, with a few intrepid climbers and skiers, but has developed into an important industry as the infrastructure has been provided for the thousands of tourists each year. Skiing and related activities are the main winter activities. The primary resources include the very attractive scenery, consisting of glaciated upland (valley glaciers), peaks, cirques, arêtes, hanging valleys, waterfalls and so on. In addition, there is sufficient snow from December to March and a variety of steepness of slopes for the ski-runs. Secondary resources include hotels, ski schools, ski-runs, restaurants and ski lifts/cable cars. The sustainability of this is open to question, as the ski-runs have destabilised the slopes, especially where the trees have been removed. Avalanches are far more frequent now and fatalities occur yearly.

Therefore, it is clear that many economic activities are carried out in glaciated areas, but the case for sustainability is far from secure.

   e This is a reasonable answer. It has an essay format, though the conclusion is poorly developed. Definitions are given, but are not totally secure. The theme of sustainability is kept to the fore, but the main limitation of this answer is the lack of support for the well-made points. In addition, summer tourism is not mentioned. Conceptually, it is good, but examples are lacking. Synopticity is present, with links to tourism in Unit 5, and this raises the mark. This is a Level 4 response (19–24 out of 30), because of the clear references to, and evaluation of, sustainability, and the use of synopticity. It is towards the lower end of this band, due to the lack of support for the points made.

     ■ ■ ■

Answer to question 6: Candidate B

Glaciated areas are defined in this essay as those areas that are currently glaciated, or those that have recently been de-glaciated. This will then include the French Alps and the Lake District in the UK. Sustainability is defined as the use of resources to meet current demand without compromising the ability of future generations to meet their own needs.

By definition, many of these areas are very fragile, especially the alpine tundra areas, where the limited diversity of species, the low temperatures and short growing season mean that it can take up to 60 years for vegetation to recover from damage. Economic activity is therefore likely to be limited in these areas.

In the Alps, tourism is the main source of income for the majority of the people. This is based on both primary and secondary resources. The primary resources include the spectacular scenery, which includes the valley glaciation landform assemblage from pyramidal peaks, arêtes, cirques, hanging valleys and waterfalls, truncated spurs, lakes and a number of depositional landforms. These are, in the opinion of many, equally spectacular in summer or winter, and tourism is a year-round activity.

The secondary resources include large numbers of hotels, restaurants, ski facilities, cable cars and the construction of ski-runs. These have enabled the resorts to become established and, with the transport infrastructure, to facilitate hundreds of thousands of visitors each year. Chamonix, in the French Alps, is a celebrated example. New hotels and ski-runs have been constructed, and the traditional activities of agriculture and forestry abandoned for more lucrative activity.

The sustainability of the industry is open to question in a number of ways. The clearance of trees and other vegetation to create the ski-runs and new tourist villages has permitted an increase in slope instability. This has coincided with an increase in the number of fatalities each year from avalanches and an increase in rock and debris slides on the steeper slopes. In addition, the increase in global temperature is causing less snow to fall and shortening the skiing season.

Hydroelectric power (HEP) is of great importance in the Alps, on large and small scales, because of the shortage of other sources of energy and the steep slopes that produce a head of water. This is very sustainable as a source of renewable energy.

In the Lake District, the issues are similar, but not completely so. There is more variety of economic activity. Tourism is a major source of income. Again, the primary resources are present, though perhaps less spectacular, as the altitude is very much lower. Large numbers of walkers climb Scafell and Helvellyn each year. The lakes themselves attract tourists, and Windermere is renowned for boating. Winter tourism is less popular and there are no major winter sports facilities. The sustainability of tourism is perhaps more likely than in the Alps. Footpath erosion and litter are problems, but they can be managed.

Agriculture is of great importance, though in recent times has seen incomes fall as the BSE and foot-and-mouth crises affected prices. Grazing of the upland pastures by hardy sheep is very important, with cattle in the lowlands. There is virtually no arable farming, but hay is taken for winter feed.

The sustainability of the industry is dependent on economic factors rather than environmental ones. The market value of livestock is low at present and this will cause farmers to go out of business. Diversification into tourism is one means of survival for some, but the foot-and-mouth restrictions also stopped tourism in this area. It is as yet uncertain whether these areas will recover fully.

Therefore, it has been demonstrated that glaciated areas provide a number of opportunities for economic development. This has been shown for the Alps and the

Lake District. The sustainability of the activities, however, does vary according to environmental and economic influences.

🖉 This is a very good response. There is a good essay style, with an introduction, definitions and a conclusion. A range of economic opportunities from two cases is used, but the detail is variable. There is good discussion of sustainability in each case and this theme is maintained throughout. Synopticity is achieved by references to elements of Unit 5 (tourism, agriculture/development). Overall, this is a very good answer, the only weakness being the lack of detail in the case studies. This is in the top Level (25–30 out of 30 marks), but is unlikely to gain full marks.